# Rainforests

## *TROPICAL AND TEMPERATE ECOSYSTEMS*

## Published by Prim-Ed Publishing

### www.prim-ed.com

6422C

*LITERACY AND GEOGRAPHY THEME*
**Rainforests**

Published by Prim-Ed Publishing® 2006
Reprinted under licence by Prim-Ed Publishing
Copyright© R.I.C. Publications® 2005
ISBN 1 84654 067 4
PR–6422

Additional titles available in this series:
**Antarctica**
**Environmental issues**
**Natural disasters**

**Internet websites**
In some cases, websites or ███████████████ ███████ checked at the time of publication, the publisher h███████████████ ██████ebpages. It is *strongly* recommended that the clas███████████████

View all pages online ████████████████████ e: www.prim-ed.com

████████████████████ sales@prim-ed.com

**Rainforests** is one of a series of four books designed specifically for upper primary pupils.

Rainforests are one of the major biomes of the world and are vital to the Earth's ecosystem. This book will help pupils to develop an in-depth understanding of the nature of this ecosystem. Units covered include defining the term 'rainforest', detailed studies of the plants and animals that make up the rainforest, exploring the Amazon and Daintree rainforests, investigating the people who live in the rainforest and the impact people are having on this precious biome.

The wide variety of activities in this book cross all major learning areas.

Titles in this series:

- *Natural disasters*
- *Rainforests*
- *Antarctica*
- *Environmental issues*

# Contents

The book has been organised into nine units, which follow a similar format.

Each unit is divided into one or more groups of four pages:

- a teachers page
- a pupil information page
- a pupil comprehension page
- a cross-curricular activity.

An **overview** for teachers has been included on pages vi – ix with suggestions for activities to further develop the theme with the whole class or as extension work for more able pupils.

## Teachers page

The teachers page has the following information:

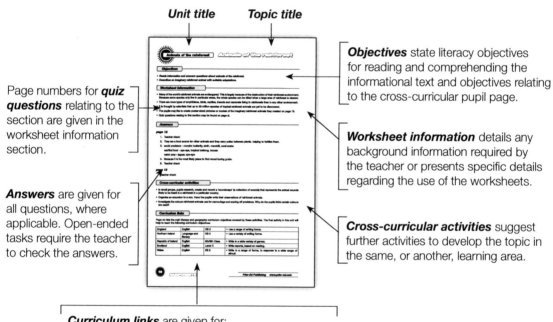

**Objectives** state literacy objectives for reading and comprehending the informational text and objectives relating to the cross-curricular pupil page.

Page numbers for **quiz questions** relating to the section are given in the worksheet information section.

**Worksheet information** details any background information required by the teacher or presents specific details regarding the use of the worksheets.

**Answers** are given for all questions, where applicable. Open-ended tasks require the teacher to check the answers.

**Cross-curricular activities** suggest further activities to develop the topic in the same, or another, learning area.

**Curriculum links** are given for:

- the geography-based theme (page xix)
- the literacy-based comprehension activity (page xix)
- the cross-curricular activity.

## Quiz questions

Quiz questions with answers are given for each section on pages x to xviii.

The quiz questions are presented in a 'half-page' card format for ease of photocopying and may be:

- given orally, with pupils answering on a separate sheet of paper,
- photocopied and given individually as a written test,
- combined with the other appropriate pages from the unit(s) as a final assessment of the topic, or
- photocopied and used by pairs or groups of pupils as 'quick quiz' activities.

The pupil pages follow the format below:

- The first pupil page is an informational text, written at a pupil's level of understanding. Illustrations and diagrams have been included where necessary to assist in their understanding of the topic being covered.

- The second pupil page is a comprehension page to gauge pupil understanding of the text. A variety of activities are provided including answering literal, deductive and evaluative questions, compiling information for a retrieval chart, completing diagrams or maps, and cloze activities.

- The final pupil page is a cross-curricular activity. Sometimes these activities may fall within the same learning area such as English.

## Pupil pages

**1.**

**Informational text** about the particular topic is provided.

**Diagrams** that assist in explaining the particular rainforest topic are included, if relevant.

Topic title    Unit title

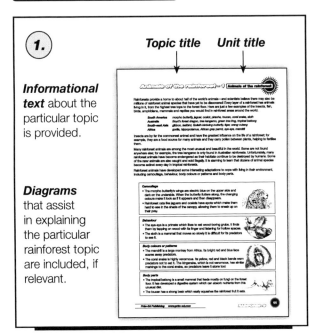

**2.**

Unit title    Topic title

**Comprehension activities** are provided to gauge pupil understanding.

**Fact file**: An interesting fact is included on pupil pages 2 and 3 to extend knowledge.

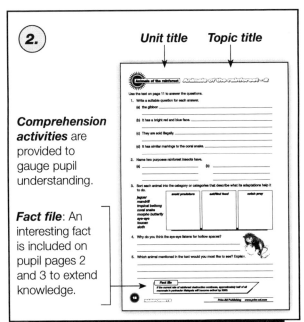

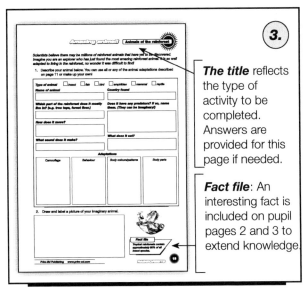

**3.**

**The title** reflects the type of activity to be completed. Answers are provided for this page if needed.

**Fact file**: An interesting fact is included on pupil pages 2 and 3 to extend knowledge.

The cross-curricular activities suggested below may aid in developing the theme.

## English

- Create a class dictionary of terms that relate specifically to rainforests.

- Write a list of similarities and differences between two rainforests; e.g. the Daintree and the Amazon.

- Plan and perform a choral speaking piece that informs people of the plight of a particular rainforest area.

- Write an acrostic, shape, cinquain, haiku or narrative poem about a rainforest.

- Pupils give other classmates the answers to questions about rainforests. The recipients must write a question to match each answer.

- Write a journal or diary entry for an animal living in the rainforest which describes the habitat, diet, hunting or gathering techniques and description of the animal.

- Create word searches, jumbled words, codes or crosswords based on clues relating to rainforests.

- Write a playscript depicting events as they may have occurred when early European explorers first discovered indigenous rainforest people.

- Write extracts from two diaries—an explorer's and an indigenous rainforest dweller's—describing their first encounter with each other.

- Conduct class debates on topics concerning rainforests. For example:

  – 'The destruction of rainforests will be the greatest problem of the 21st century'

  – 'Four-wheel drive tracks should be constructed through rainforests, such as the Daintree, so that tourists can explore the spectacular environment'

  – 'Part of all rainforests should be used for timber to provide employment and boost that country's economy'.

- Write letters to newspapers expressing concern about the future of rainforests.

## Maths

- Compile a list of mathematical facts about rainforests; e.g. 'About 90% of West Africa's rainforest has been destroyed by humans'.

- Use scale measurements to create accurate representations of rainforest scenes using models of rainforest plants and animals.

- Compare the amount of rainforest in countries in South America that are part of the Amazon Basin. Some of these include Brazil, Venezuela, Ecuador, Suriname, Bolivia, Colombia and Guyana.

- Compile time lines of explorations into various rainforests.

- Rank countries where rainforests are found in order from most to least areas of rainforest.

- Create mathematical problems for specific rainforest areas; for example, 'If there are 2000 hectares of rainforest and 10% has been destroyed, how many hectares are left?

- Research data and create a graph to show how the total area of rainforest has declined in the last 150 years. Use this graph to determine how long it will be before rainforests disappear if the current trend continues.

- Research and graph the average monthly rainfall in particular rainforests.

- Draw two line graphs comparing the average monthly temperatures of a tropical and a temperate rainforest.

- Calculate the distance between the pupils' community and a particular rainforest.

- Create a table that compares the statistics (land area, average rainfall, number of endangered and threatened species, average temperate etc.) between the Amazon rainforest and the Daintree rainforest.

- Conduct a survey to determine pupils' favourite rainforest animal. Give pupils a list to choose from and include an 'other' category. Tally the results and display as a bar chart. Ensure the graph has a title, labelled axes and a consistent scale.

The cross-curricular activities suggested below may aid in developing the theme.

## Geography and history

- Create more detailed maps than those on pages 7 and 9 to show specific areas of tropical and temperate rainforests.

- Collect photographs of rainforests from images on the Internet and in magazines to form a mural labelled with information. Include images of people and artefacts.

- In small groups, research to prepare written and other materials that educate people about conserving rainforests.

- Research and write information about indigenous people of different rainforest areas.

- Draw flow charts to show how specific plants or animals form part of the cycle of life in a rainforest.

- Create 'before' and 'after' maps which show areas of rainforests on continents 100 years ago and today.

- Label a world map with early exploration routes from Europe to illustrate when and from where the discovery of rainforests occurred.

- Present information detailing which European nations had the greatest influence on different areas of rainforest. Explain how the lives of the indigenous people have been affected by these changes.

- Research the timber industry to discover how logging is conducted in the rainforest; e.g. in Ketchikan, Alaska, logs are carried out of the forest by helicopter as this is cheaper than building access roads.

- Compile a list of reasons for and against the clearing of rainforests.

- Research and list the criteria for an area to become listed as a World Heritage area. (Hint: There are four criteria.)

- What is ecotourism? Investigate in small groups.

## Science

- Research to find out the different animals and plants found in tropical and temperate rainforests.

- Investigate how the rainforest experiences of English naturalist, Charles Darwin, helped to shape his theory of evolution through natural selection.

- Construct food chains and food webs for tropical and temperate rainforests.

- Invite a medical expert to speak to the class about medicines made from rainforest plants.

- Examine the movements of a range of rainforest animals and compare them to human movements.

- Research to find out about some special adaptations of unusual rainforest animals.

- Select a specific rainforest plant used for drugs or medicines; investigate its growing patterns, cultivation and conversion for medical use.

- Create experiments to show how the rainforest receives and uses rain.

- Research to discover how different adaptations enable plants to thrive in tropical rainforest conditions.

- Research to discover any relationship between particular species of plants and animals in the rainforest; e.g. panda/bamboo.

- Write a report on an animal found in the rainforest.

- Research how excessive rainfall leaches minerals from the soils of tropical rainforests.

- Explain the process of transpiration. Include diagrams.

- Hold a discussion about the reasons why pupils think the dinosaurs became extinct but flora (such as the primitive flora found in the Daintree rainforest) did not.

- Investigate the methods of seed dispersal among rainforest plants. Draw diagrams to show how seeds disperse. Methods include wind, water, by animal and by discharge (exploding).

- Use a dictionary to determine the difference among a biologist, a botanist, a geologist and an ecologist.

- Research to discover why mangroves are unique. Sketch a mangrove and label its components.

The cross-curricular activities suggested below may aid in developing the theme.

## The arts

### (Music, drama, visual arts)

- Create and perform a soundscape for a tropical or temperate rainforest. The animals which live in each will need to be researched first.

- Create collages of tropical and temperate rainforests where creatures and plants are camouflaged within the foliage.

- Create dioramas or collages that demonstrate the different layers of a rainforest.

- Make puppets of rainforest animals suitable for young children. Use them to plan and perform a puppet show for a younger class at the school.

- Write a rap about a rainforest and add movements before presenting it to the class or school.

- Design and create costumes to depict plants from different layers of the rainforest and use them to show the growth, destruction and renewal of the rainforest.

- With particular plants and animals as subjects, use a range of art techniques and materials to present a display of vivid textures and colours found in the rainforest.

- Create a poster titled 'Save our rainforests'.

- Dramatise the confrontation between a group of conservationists and the employees of a logging company in a rainforest.

- Use the Internet and books to find a picture of a colourful parrot that lives in a rainforest. Trace the picture of the parrot onto an overhead sheet and project and enlarge it using an overhead projector onto a whiteboard. On a large sheet of paper, trace the parrot. Pupils use square pieces of coloured paper and glue just the top part on to the parrot so they resemble its feathers. Display on a wall.

## Health and personal/social development

- Write healthy recipes using only ingredients that have originated in rainforests.

- Invite a guest speaker from an environmental organisation concerned with conserving rainforests. Discuss the organisation's values and whether the pupils think they are important.

- Investigate drugs which have been created from rainforest plants and how they are used.

- Investigate and draw diagrams which show how the destruction of the rainforest affects atmospheric conditions and, consequently, the lives of people on Earth.

- Discuss and record the benefits of living in a close tribal community; e.g. care, discipline, education, maintaining traditions.

- Make lists of foods eaten by different native groups, noting similarities and differences.

- List some of the health concerns of visitors to a tropical rainforest.

- Plan a medical kit for an Amazon rainforest visitor.

- If climbing ropes are available, ask pupils to climb the rope and imagine it is a vine in a rainforest. As the pupil is climbing, he/she must describe which types of flora and fauna he/she is seeing at each level of the rainforest.

- Discuss how the health of a species is affected once part of a rainforest is destroyed. Discuss the meanings of the words ecosystem, food chain, habitat and food web. Explain how if one species on a food chain disappears, other species in the chain are threatened.

The cross-curricular activities suggested below may aid in developing the theme.

### DT and ICT

- Design a 'hide' scientists could use to observe rainforest animals without being discovered.

- Compile a list of websites which investigate both sides of the rainforest argument.

- Design a travel brochure for a particular rainforest. Include 'Dos and Don'ts' to protect the rainforest.

- Investigate and research, using the Internet, organisations which aim to save the rainforest.

- Design a range of materials to support a campaign to help save the rainforests.

- Design a postage stamp that informs people about an endangered rainforest animal or plant.

- Create a model of a specific rainforest from a design.

- From research information, make models of different types of tribal houses found in particular rainforests around the world. List building materials used by the people and explain why the design suits the conditions.

- Make models of cooking facilities used by indigenous people of the rainforest.

- Design a house suitable for the climate of a tropical or temperate rainforest, incorporating some locally available building materials.

- Design an outfit to be worn in a tropical or temperate rainforest. Give careful consideration to all the environmental factors.

- Create an 'Internet challenge' (similar to the one on page 53), about the fauna of the rainforest. Give it to a classmate to complete.

- Design a treetop walk that causes the minimum amount of disturbance to a rainforest and uses materials and colours that blend into the environment.

1. A tropical rainforest climate

   is _____ and

   _____ and a

   temperate rainforest climate is

   _____ .

2. What helps to supply moisture to a temperate rainforest in the drier, warmer months?

   _____

3. What types of leaves would many trees have in a ...

   (a) tropical rainforest?

   _____

   (b) temperate rainforest?

   _____

4. List the layers of a temperate rainforest from the lowest to the highest layer.

   _____

   _____

   _____

5. Trees live between 50 and 100 years in a (tropical, temperate) rainforest.

   _____

6. What fraction of the Earth's plant and animal species live in rainforests?

   _____

7. Which type of rainforest has more animals?

   _____

- - - - - - - - - - - - - - - - - - - - - - - - - - - - - - - - - - - - - - - - - - - - - - - - - - - - - - ✂

**QUIZ** **Where are rainforests found?**

**Pages 6–9**

1. Fill in the missing words.

   (a) Tropical rainforests are found close to the _____ between

   the Tropic of _____ and the Tropic of _____ .

   (b) Temperate rainforests generally lie on _____ coastal

   mountains in the _____ zone.

2. What type of rainforest is more widespread?    ☐ tropical    ☐ temperate

3. For a biome to be considered a rainforest, it must have a minimum of

   (1000, 1500, 2000, 3000) mm of rain per year.

4. List four areas or countries in the world where tropical rainforests are found.

   _____        _____

   _____        _____

5. List four areas or countries in the world where temperate rainforests are found.

   _____        _____

   _____        _____

## QUIZ — Animals of the rainforest

1. Which group of animals is the most common in a rainforest?

   (a) mammals (b) insects (c) amphibians

   _____

2. What type of animal is an ocelot?

   _____

3. What makes it difficult to see a sloth?

   _____

4. Scientist believe there are millions more rainforest animal species left to be discovered.

   True ◯  False ◯

5. Which animal taps on wood and listens for hollow spaces to find wood-boring grubs?

   _____

6. Name two ways in which rainforest animals have adapted to cope with living in their environment.

   _____

   _____

7. Name the body part of these animals which helps them survive in the rainforest.

   (a) tropical bettong

   _____

   (b) toucan

   _____

8. What is the name of the butterfly which appears to change colour as it flutters?

   _____

✂ - - - - - - - - - - - - - - - - - - - - - - - - - - - - - - - - - - - - - - - - - - - - - - - - - -

## QUIZ — Colossal cassowaries, fatal frogs and odd okapis

1. Which part of its body does a cassowary use to defend itself?_____

2. What protects the cassowary's eyes from leaves and twigs?_____

3. What is the nature of the Southern cassowary? _____

4. What type of food makes up the main diet of the cassowary? _____

5. In which continent does the poison arrow frog live? _____

6. How do native rainforest people obtain the poison from the poison arrow frog?

   _____

   _____

7. In which year was the okapi discovered by Western scientists?

   (a) 1501          (b) 1901          (c) 2001

8. The okapi is the only living relative of which animal? _____

9. What colour is the tongue of an okapi? _____

10. How long is the tongue of the okapi? _____

11. The main predator of the okapi is the _____.

## QUIZ — Big butterflies, scary snakes and magnificent monkeys

**Pages 18–21**

1. The Queen Alexandra's birdwing is the largest _____ in the world.

2. What plant does the female butterfly lay its eggs on?
   _____

3. Why is it difficult to find out how many birdwing butterflies there are?
   _____
   _____

4. The anaconda eats its prey whole.
   True   False

5. What enables anacondas to hide underwater?
   _____

6. Name the two colours of the colobus monkey's fur.
   _____

7. Approximately what length can an anaconda grow to? (Tick your answer.)
   (a)  2 metres   ☐
   (b)  5 metres   ☐
   (c)  9 metres   ☐

8. What does a colobus monkey lack that most other monkeys have?
   _____

9. The greatest threat to the colobus monkey is _____

---

✂

## QUIZ — Plants of the rainforest

**Pages 22–25**

1. What fraction of the world's plants grow in the tropical rainforests?   ☐

2. Which parts of plants change to adapt to the rainforest conditions?
   _____

3. What percentage of the developed world's diet comes from the rainforest?   ☐

4. Name three other reasons for the importance of the rainforest.
   (a) _____
   (b) _____
   (c) _____

5. What are the four main layers of the tropical rainforest?
   _____     _____
   _____     _____

6. ☐ per cent of Western drugs come from rainforest plants.

Prim-Ed Publishing    www.prim-ed.com

## Quiz — Plant profiles

1. Write two words to describe the conditions in the tropical rainforest.

_____

_____

2. Write two words to describe the soil in the rainforest.

_____

_____

3. The roots of plants in the rainforest are usually

_____

4. Name three different types of roots which help some rainforest plants to stay upright and to get nutrients.

_____

_____

_____

5. Write the names of the following plants:

   (a) organisms which grow on dead and decaying plants

   _____

   (b) thick, woody vines

   _____

   (c) air plants which grow on other plants to get to the sun

   _____

6. One example of a liana is a

   _____

7. One example of an epiphyte is a

   _____

## Quiz — People of the rainforest

1. Tick 'true' or 'false'.

   (a) Rainforest homes are simple.  True ◯ False ◯

   (b) Electrical goods are widely used in rainforest areas.  True ◯ False ◯

   (c) Only men and boys go hunting.  True ◯ False ◯

   (d) All people of the rainforests speak many languages.  True ◯ False ◯

2. Name two essential skills for the hunting party.

   _____

   _____

   _____

   _____

3. What jobs do young children do in the rainforest?

   _____

4. Why are houses built with raised floors?

   _____

   _____

   _____

5. What do children learn even if they do not attend school?

   _____

   _____

## QUIZ — Traditional rainforest tribes

1. Name two tribes which live in the Brazilian rainforests.

   _____

   _____

3. In the Tukano tribe, what are men and women named after?

   _____

   _____

4. What is the name of the communal house in which the Yanomami live?

   _____

5. What does the Mbuti use to track down beehives? _____

6. What does the sacred ritual of 'molimo' of the Mbuti tribe celebrate?

   _____

7. Molimo can also be _____

2. 'True' or 'false':

   (a) The Mbuti are generally tall people. ☐

   (b) Rainforest people are very knowledgeable about rainforest plants. ☐

   (c) Yanomami hunters never eat the meat they have caught themselves. ☐

---

## QUIZ — The Amazon rainforest

1. Name any two of the countries in which the Amazon rainforest is found.

   _____

   _____

2. Why has the Amazon rainforest been described as the 'lungs of our planet'?

   _____

   _____

   _____

3. Where does the Amazon River start?

   _____

4. Describe the climate of the Amazon rainforest.

   _____

   _____

5. What was the easiest way to travel into the Amazon rainforest?

   _____

   _____

6. What causes millions of hectares of rainforest to be underwater for months?

   _____

   _____

   _____

7. What is the Amazon rainforest called in Brazil?

   _____

8. How big is the Amazon Rainforest?

   _____

1. What has made the soils of the Amazon rainforest infertile?

_____

_____

_____

2. Why is the rainforest being cleared?

_____

_____

_____

3. Where in the rainforest do fruits and flowers grow?

_____

4. Why aren't there lots of plants growing on the floor of the rainforest?

_____

_____

5. Why are plants growing in the rainforest so important?

_____

_____

_____

6. Why is the clearing of the rainforest a problem?

_____

_____

_____

_____

✂ ------------------------------------------------------------

***Tick 'true' or 'false'.***

True / False  1. Christopher Columbus discovered the Amazon.

True / False  2. The Amazon was named by the Spanish explorer, Orellana.

True / False  3. Charles Darwin thought that the Amazon rainforest was a most interesting and exciting place.

True / False  4. Amazon was the name of one of the tribes living in the Amazon rainforest.

True / False  5. The country of Brazil was named after some red-wood trees found growing there.

True / False  6. Charles Darwin was a famous sea captain.

True / False  7. Alexander von Humboldt conducted the first scientific tests on an electric eel he found swimming in the river.

True / False  8. Adventurers searched the Amazon rainforest for the city of El Dorado because they believed that there was treasure there.

1. Circle the year in which Sir Joseph Banks first made a record of the area now known as the Daintree rainforest.

    (a) 1770        (b) 1897        (c) 1930

2. In which state of Australia is the Daintree rainforest found?

    _____

3. In the 1930s, many changes occurred to the Daintree rainforest. List two of these changes.

    • _____

      _____

      _____

    • _____

      _____

      _____

4. Which medical condition do scientists believe rainforest plants may help to cure?

    _____

5. (a) How many species of birds have been recorded in the Daintree rainforest?

    _____

    (b) How many of these species are found nowhere else in the world?

    _____

------------------------------------------------------------------ ✂

 **Fauna of the Daintree**

**Pages 54–57**

1. List two creatures the rufous owl preys upon.

    _____ and

    _____

2. Which animal found in the Daintree rainforest has a mating call that resembles a dog's bark?

    _____

3. Who am I?

    > • I am nocturnal.
    >
    > • I eat spiders and worms from the forest floor.
    >
    > • I hop like a kangaroo.
    >
    > • I have a long nose.
    >
    >   I am a _____ .

4. True or false: A cassowary can only fly short distances. ☐

5. How is a spotted cuscus able to hang upside down from trees?

    _____

    _____

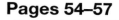

## QUIZ The destruction of the rainforest

*State true or false.*

| | 1. | Rainforests are complex ecosystems. |
| | 2. | The population of the world has increased by 40% since 1980. |
| | 3. | As population increases so does the demand for commercial rainforest goods. |
| | 4. | Subsistence farmers clear land for crops and it becomes more fertile each year. |
| | 5. | The largest cause of rainforest destruction is commercial logging. |
| | 6. | Cattle grazing and large-scale agriculture projects do not worsen the rainforest problem. |
| | 7. | Destroying the rainforest affects plants, animals, indigenous people, the soil, water and air. |

- - - - - - - - - - - - - - - - - - - - - - - - - - - - - - - - - - - - - - - - - - - - - - - - -

## QUIZ Preserving the rainforest

*Write words to complete the sentences.*

1. The rainforest is home to 50 to 70% of

   all _____

2. Many plants and animals from the rainforest are now endangered or

   _____

3. Many life-saving drugs may never be discovered because the

   _____

   from which they come have been destroyed.

4. Rainforests use the process of

   _____

   to capture, store and recycle rain.

5. Experts believe that the destruction of the rainforest causes

   _____

   around the world.

6. The removal of the protective layer of dead and decaying material can create

   _____

   _____

7. Over 1000 or more groups of

   _____

   around the world may be on the verge of extinction due to the destruction of their rainforest.

# Quiz answers

### What is a rainforest?...2–5

1. warm and humid; cool
2. coastal fog
3. (a) broad leaves
   (b) needle-shaped
4. forest floor, understorey, canopy
5. tropical
6. half
7. tropical

### Where are rainforests found?..........................6–9

1. (a) Equator; Cancer; Capricorn
   (b) west-facing; Temperate
2. tropical
3. 2000
4. Teacher check
5. Teacher check

### Animals of the rainforest................10–13

1. (b) insects
2. a cat
3. It moves slowly.
4. true
5. the aye-aye
6. Answers may include: camouflage, body colours and patterns, body parts, behaviour.
7. (a) digestive system
   (b) beak
8. morpho butterfly

### Colossal cassowaries, fatal frogs and odd okapis ......................14–17

1. its toenails
2. the bony helmet on its head
3. shy, solitary
4. fruit
5. South America
6. They wipe their arrows or darts onto the frog's skin.
7. (b) 1901
8. the giraffe
9. blue-black
10. the length of a ruler
11. leopard

### Big butterflies, scary snakes and magnificent monkeys .................18–21

1. butterfly
2. pipe vine
3. because they fly and feed up high
4. true
5. They have eyes and nostrils on top of their heads.
6. black and white
7. (c) 9 metres
8. a thumb
9. rainforest destruction by humans

### Plants of the rainforest.................22–25

1. two-thirds
2. roots, bark, leaves, trunks
3. 80%
4. (a) oxygen for the earth
   (b) ingredients for drugs and medicines
   (c) rubber, chemicals, materials for baskets or rope
5. emergent, canopy, understorey, undergrowth
6. 25%

### Plant profiles ..........26–29

1. hot, wet
2. thin, poor
3. shallow
4. buttress, prop, stilt
5. (a) saprophytes
   (b) lianas
   (c) epiphytes
6. philodendron
7. fern/orchid/bromeliad

### People of the rainforest ................................30–33

1. (a) true (b) false
   (c) true (d) false
2. recognising the signs of animals; following animals quietly
3. collect firewood, fruit
4. to keep things protected from the wet forest floor
5. essential skills for living in the rainforest

### Traditional rainforest tribes .....................34–37

1. Yanomami, Tukano
2. (a) false
   (b) true
   (c) true
3. men–birds; women–plants
4. yano
5. Greater Honeyguide bird
6. giving thanks to the forest for what it provides
7. a trumpet-like musical instrument

### The Amazon rainforest ................................38–41

1. Brazil, Colombia, Peru, Bolivia, Venezuela, Ecuador, the Guyanas
2. It produces 20% of the world's oxygen by recycling carbon dioxide.
3. Peruvian Andes
4. hot, wet and humid
5. along rivers
6. The snow on the mountains melts and floods the rainforest.
7. Amazonia
8. about the size of Australia

### Plants and animals of the Amazon....................42–45

1. excessive rainfall has taken the nutrients out of the soil
2. logging, mining, cattle ranches, agriculture
3. in the canopy
4. There isn't enough sunlight reaching the ground.
5. Many of them have been found useful for making medicines.
6. the survival of many species of animals and plants and the importance of the oxygen produced by the rainforest

### Exploring the Amazon....................46–49

1. false
2. true
3. true
4. false
5. true
6. false
7. true
8. true

### Discovering the Daintree.................50–53

1. (a) 1770
2. Queensland
3. • families settled on the land,
   • fruit was grown— bananas, watermelon and pineapple
   • timber industry began
4. cancer
5. (a) 430 (b) 13

### Fauna of the Daintree.................54–57

1. blue-winged kookaburra, flying foxes, sugar gliders, cockatoos and beetles
2. Giant tree frog
3. bandicoot
4. false – it's flightless
5. It uses it two-thumbed hands.

### The destruction of the rainforest................58–61

1. true   5. true
2. false  6. false
3. true   7. true
4. false

### Preserving the rainforest................62–65

1. life forms
2. extinct
3. plants
4. evaporation
5. climate change
6. human-made deserts
7. indigenous people

The units of activities throughout this book will help to teach the following literacy and geography curriculum objectives.

The final activity in each unit provides either a literacy, geography or cross-curricular activity that covers other curriculum objectives. The curriculum links for these activities are listed on the relevant accompanying pages of teachers notes.

| England | English | KS 2 | • Read a range of non-fiction texts.<br>• Engage with challenging subject matter.<br>• Obtain specific information through detailed reading. |
|---|---|---|---|
| | Geography | KS 2 | • Study a range of places and environments in different parts of the world.<br>• Identify location of places, what places are like, how and why places change and how places compare to other places.<br>• Recognise human processes and how these can cause changes in environments and how and why people may seek to manage environments sustainably. |
| Northern Ireland | Language and literacy | KS 2 | • Engage in a wide range of reading activities for a variety of purposes.<br>• Use a variety of reading skills. |
| | Geography | KS 2 | • Study, compare and contrast different places and environments.<br>• Know about the use of natural resources in the environment and the importance of conserving them, such as the rainforests. |
| Republic of Ireland | English | 5th/6th Class | • Read a more challenging range of reading material, including non-fiction texts.<br>• Use comprehension skills. |
| | Geography | 5th/6th Class | • Become familiar with the distinctive natural features of places in other parts of the world.<br>• Recognise and investigate aspects of human activities which have adverse effects on the environment, including globally; for example, deforestation. |
| Scotland | English | Level C/D | • Use an increasing range of non-fiction texts.<br>• Read for specific information. |
| | Society | Level C/D | • Extend the mental map further to include world features and locations.<br>• Identify and describe a range of physical features found outside Scotland.<br>• For a selected land use change, describe possible effects, good and bad, on the landscape/environment; e.g. tropical forest clearance. |
| Wales | English | KS 2 | • Read a range of non-fiction texts.<br>• Read for information from challenging texts.<br>• Read for different purposes, including detailed reading to obtain specific information. |
| | Geography | KS 2 | • Study contrasting localities, including where it is, what its like, why its like this, how it compares to other places and how its changing.<br>• Identify ways in which people affect the environment and how to safeguard the future environment through sustainable development. |

What is a rainforest?

## Objectives

- Reads information and answers questions about a rainforest biome.
- Compares a tropical and a temperate rainforest by completing a retrieval chart.

## Worksheet information

- Tropical rainforests are millions of years old, while temperate rainforests are about 10 000 years old. The former are more widespread, covering about six per cent of the Earth's surface. Tropical rainforests in particular have an abundance of plant and animal life, more than any other biome. The relationship between the plants and animals in a rainforest is one of the most complex. Any slight upset to the balance can cause severe problems for the plants and animals which rely on the rainforest for survival—making this ecosystem extremely vulnerable.
- Pupils will need a dictionary to complete Question 1 on page 4.
- Quiz questions relating to this section can be found on page x.

## Answers

**page 4**

1. (a) a large area of distinctive plant and animal groups that are adapted to that physical environment
   (b) of or found in the tropics, an area surrounding the Equator
   (c) moderate in terms of temperature
   (d) a community of living things interacting with one another and the environment in which they live
2. Answers will vary but could include: lots of tall trees, lots of animals, lots of plants, heavy rainfall, wet environment, rainforest grows in layers
3. A tropical rainforest has a warm, humid climate and a temperate rainforest has a cool climate.
4. (a) true (b) true (c) false (d) false (e) true (f) false
5. The canopy of tall trees above these levels forms a 'roof' which prevents sunlight from penetrating.
6. plants produce much of the Earth's oxygen; help maintain global weather patterns; provide a home to about half the plant and animal species in the world

**page 5**

| | Tropical rainforest | Temperate rainforest |
|---|---|---|
| **Location** | close to the Equator | along the coasts in temperate zones |
| **Climate** | warm and humid | cool |
| **Amount of annual rainfall** | 2000 mm–10 000 mm | 2000–3000 mm depending on latitude |
| **When does it rain?** | throughout the year | mostly in winter |
| **Temperature** | 25 °C–30 °C all year round | rarely over 25 °C in summer, much cooler in winter |
| **Facts about animals** | huge variety, most live in trees | much less variety, most live on or near the forest floor |
| **Facts about trees** | hundreds of species, live between 50 and 100 years, broad leaves | 10–20 species, live between 500–1000 years, needle-shaped leaves |
| **Description of forest layers** | emergent, canopy, understorey and forest floor | canopy, understorey and forest floor |

## Cross-curricular activities

- Pupils can use the Internet, magazines or nonfiction material to find illustrations of animals, trees and plants belonging to each rainforest. These can be displayed and labelled with interesting facts.
- After viewing the illustrations as above, pupils can brainstorm to list words and phrases to describe each kind of rainforest. They can then identify the same words or phrases they used in their descriptions.
- In groups, pupils can investigate other major biomes such as a desert, alpine region, grassland, savannah, wetland or marine environment. A report could be collated to share with the class.

## Curriculum links

Page xix lists the main literacy and geography curriculum objectives covered by these activities. The final activity in this unit will help to teach the following curriculum objectives:

| England | English | KS 2 | • Use scanning and detailed reading of texts to find information and use a range of writing forms. |
|---|---|---|---|
| Northern Ireland | Language and literacy | KS 2 | • Use a variety of reading skills and experiment with different writing formats. |
| Republic of Ireland | English | 5th/6th Class | • Use comprehension and study skills and write in a wide variety of genres. |
| Scotland | English | Level C/D | • Scan texts for specific information and present information in varied formats. |
| Wales | English | KS 2 | • Use scanning and detailed reading of texts to find information and use the characteristics of different kinds of writing. |

Rainforests are one of the major biomes of the world. A biome is a large area of distinctive plant and animal groups that are adapted to that physical environment. Other major biomes include deserts, grasslands, alpine and aquatic environments.

When we hear the word 'rainforest', we imagine lots of tall trees, lots of plants, lots of animals and lots of rain. There are also a number of other features that make a biome a rainforest.

Most people think of a rainforest as being a warm and humid place, but this is not always true. There are actually two types of rainforests. One is known as a tropical rainforest, where the climate is warm and humid. The other is a known as a temperate rainforest, and, while it is also very wet, the climate is cool.

*Tropical rainforests* are found close to the Equator and can receive from 2000 to 10 000 mm of rain, which is evenly distributed throughout the year. The average temperature ranges from about 25 °C to 30 °C all year round. In a tropical rainforest, there are hundreds of species of trees. They live between 50 and 100 years and many have broad leaves. A huge variety of animals live in this rainforest, with most of them living in the trees.

*Temperate rainforests* are found along the western coasts of some countries in temperate zones. They receive at least 2000 to 3000 mm of rain each year, but this amount can be higher depending on latitude. There are wet (winter) and dry

(summer) seasons in a temperate rainforest. Coastal summer fogs keep the forests cool and supply moisture during the drier warmer months. The temperature is cooler than a tropical rainforest, rarely getting over 25 °C in summer and becoming much cooler in winter—it can even snow in some areas. In a temperate rainforest there are at most 10 to 20 species of trees. They live between 500 to 1000 years and many have needle-shaped leaves. Temperate rainforests do not have as wide a variety of animals as the tropical type and most of these live on or near the forest floor.

Both rainforests grow in layers, with different plants and animals living in each.

**Emergent layer:** This is found only in a tropical rainforest. It has giant trees that grow much higher than the rest of the forest and receive the most sunlight.

**Canopy:** Tall trees growing close together so they form a shady 'roof' over the rainforest.

**Understorey:** A dark environment consisting of smaller trees, bushes and plants such as ferns.

**Forest floor:** A very dark area covered with fallen leaves, twigs and logs.

Rainforests are vital to the Earth's ecosystem. The plants of the rainforest produce much of the Earth's oxygen. They also help maintain global weather patterns, as water that evaporates from the trees falls in other areas as rain. Rainforests provide a home for about half of the plant and animal species in the world, many of which are the most unusual found anywhere.

Use the text on page 3 to answer the questions.

1. Use the text and a dictionary to write a definition for each word.

   (a) biome _____

   _____

   (b) tropical _____

   (c) temperate _____

   (d) ecosystem _____

   _____

2. List five general features which make a biome a rainforest.

   _____

   _____

   _____

   _____

3. What is the difference in climate between a tropical and a temperate rainforest?

   _____

   _____

   _____

   _____

4. Tick 'true' or 'false'.

   (a) Tropical rainforests receive more rain than temperate rainforests. True  False

   (b) Trees live longer in a temperate rainforest. True  False

   (c) A tropical rainforest can experience snow. True  False

   (d) Temperate rainforests have only one season. True  False

   (e) Most animals in a tropical rainforest live in trees. True  False

   (f) The understorey layer of a rainforest receives the least sunlight. True  False

5. What helps to make the understorey and forest floor dark environments?

   _____

   _____

6. Give three reasons why rainforests are important to the Earth's ecosystem.

   • _____

   • _____

   • _____

**Fact file**

*The term 'tropical rainforest' was first used in 1898 by a German botanist, Andreas Franz Schimper. It comes from the German 'tropische regenweld'.*

 **Rainforest retrieval chart**  **What is a rainforest?**

Use the text on page 3 and your own words and phrases to complete this retrieval chart showing the differences between tropical and temperate rainforests.

|  | Tropical rainforest | Temperate rainforest |
|---|---|---|
| **Location** |  |  |
| **Climate** |  |  |
| **Amount of annual rainfall** |  |  |
| **When does it rain?** |  |  |
| **Temperature** |  |  |
| **Facts about animals** |  |  |
| **Facts about trees** |  |  |
| **Description of forest layers** |  |  |

**Fact file**

The tallest living tree is a redwood found in a temperate rainforest in northern California, USA. It is 112 metres in height and over 1000 years old.

## Objectives

• *Reads information and answers questions about where rainforests are found.*

• *Creates a colour key for a map and locates places on a map with the assistance of an atlas.*

## Worksheet information

• Pupils will need an atlas to complete the activities on pages 8 and 9.

• Quiz questions relating to this section can be found on page x.

## Answers

### page 8

1. The 'tropics' refers to the band circling the Earth between the Tropic of Cancer and the Tropic of Capricorn.

2. The Temperate zone is situated north of the Tropic of Cancer and south of the Tropic of Capricorn.

3. The sun shines directly over the Equator so temperatures are high. The heat from the direct sunlight causes excessive amounts of water to be evaporated which rises then falls as rain when it cools.

4. West-facing coastal mountain areas receive moisture-laden winds from the ocean, resulting in very high rainfall necessary for a rainforest and fogs in the drier season.

5. Answers may vary but could include:

   (a) There are *fewer* temperate rainforests than temperate forests.

   (b) A rainforest has to receive a minimum of *2000 mm* of rain per year.

   (c) The largest area of temperate rainforest is in *North America*.

   (d) Europe has *no* areas of tropical rainforest.

6. Possible answer: There are no coastal mountain ranges high enough to assist with the amount of rainfall needed to be classified as a rainforest.

7. Possible answers: It is too cold for trees to grow; not enough rain falls in Antarctica.

### page 9

Teacher check

## Cross-curricular activities

• Pupils can research to find out the names of other countries in South America, Central America, South-East Asia and Africa that contain tropical rainforest and the states and provinces in North America that contain temperate rainforest.

• Use a globe and a torch to demonstrate how the sun shines directly over the Equator, with seasonal variation causing winter and summer at different times in the Northern and Southern Hemispheres.

## Curriculum links

Page xix lists the main literacy and geography curriculum objectives covered by these activities. The final activity in this unit will help to teach the following curriculum objectives:

| England | Geography | KS 2 | • Use atlases and know the location of the environments they study. |
|---|---|---|---|
| Northern Ireland | Geography | KS 2 | • Locate all places studied in atlases. |
| Republic of Ireland | Geography | 5th/6th Class | • Engage in practical use of maps and develop an understanding of the names and locations of major natural features. |
| Scotland | Society | Level C | • Identify world locations on a map. |
| Wales | Geography | KS 2 | • Locate places using atlases. |

*Tropical rainforests* are generally located close to the Equator, between the Tropic of Cancer and the Tropic of Capricorn. This band circling the Earth is known as the 'tropics'. The sun shines most directly over the Equator, so temperatures near the Equator are high. The heat from the direct sunlight causes excessive amounts of water to be evaporated into the air. As it rises, it cools, resulting in frequent rain, particularly in forested areas. It is always warm, humid and wet in a tropical rainforest, though there is usually a brief season of less rain.

### Tropical rainforests can be found in the following locations around the world.

- Central America and the Amazon River Basin in South America.
- Zaire Basin in central Africa, a small area in West Africa and eastern Madagascar.
- Indo-Malaysia – west coast of India and South-East Asia.
- Much of New Guinea and parts of north-eastern Australia and nearby islands.

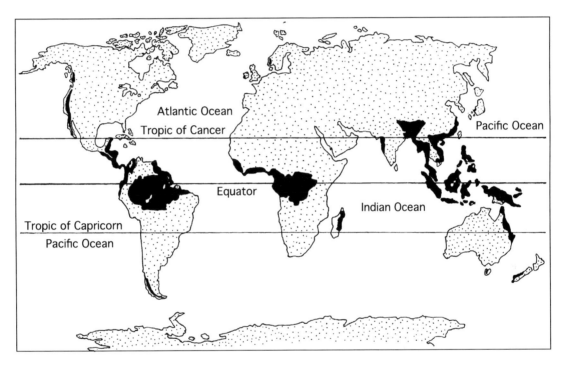

*Temperate rainforests* are found along the coasts of some countries in the Temperate Zone, which is north of the Tropic of Cancer and south of the Tropic of Capricorn. Temperate forests cover a large part of the world but temperate *rainforests* are found in only a few places. For a biome to be considered a rainforest there has to be a minimum of 2000 mm of rain per year. Temperate rainforests generally lie on west-facing coastal mountains or slopes which receive moisture-laden winds from the ocean, resulting in high rainfall in the long, wet, winter months. The proximity to the ocean also means that temperate rainforests have fogs that provide moisture in the short, dry, summer season.

### Temperate rainforests can mostly be found in the following locations.

- Along the Pacific coast of North America.
- Chile, in South America.
- Parts of the west coast of the South Island of New Zealand.
- Parts of the west coast of Tasmania, Australia.
- Parts of south-western Japan.
- Very small areas in the west of Ireland, Scotland and Norway.

Use the text and map on page 7 and an atlas to answer the questions.

1. Where is the area known as the 'tropics' situated?

   _____

   _____

2. Where is the area known as the 'Temperate Zone' situated?

   _____

   _____

3. Explain why there is heavy rainfall in areas near the Equator.

   _____

   _____

   _____

   _____

4. Why are temperate rainforests found generally on west-facing coastal

   mountains or slopes? _____

   _____

   _____

5. Rewrite these statements so they are correct.

   (a) There are more temperate rainforests than temperate forests.

   _____

   _____

   (b) A rainforest has to receive a minimum of 1000 mm of rain per year.

   _____

   _____

   (c) The largest area of temperate rainforest is in South America.

   _____

   _____

   (d) Europe has extensive areas of tropical rainforest.

   _____

   _____

6. Why do you think temperate rainforests are not found on the west coast of

   Australia?_____

   _____

7. Why do you think rainforests are not found in Antarctica? _____

   _____

---

**Fact file**

*Tropical rainforests are found in 85 countries, with 90 per cent of them in 15 countries.*

Use the information on page 7 and an atlas to complete the activities below.

1. (a) Create a colour key to shade the major areas of tropical and temperate rainforest on the map.

   (b) Decide in which type of rainforest the places below can be found. Use the same colour key to label each place on the map.

| | | | |
|---|---|---|---|
| ☐ Zaire Basin | ☐ New Zealand | ☐ Chile | |
| ☐ Japan | ☐ Amazon Basin | ☐ India | |
| ☐ North America | ☐ New Guinea | ☐ Vietnam | |
| ☐ Australia | ☐ Central America | ☐ Philippines | |
| ☐ Malaysia | ☐ Indonesia | ☐ Thailand | |
| ☐ Myanmar (Burma) | ☐ South-East China | ☐ Madagascar | |
| ☐ Ireland | ☐ Scotland | | |
| ☐ Norway | ☐ Tasmania | | |

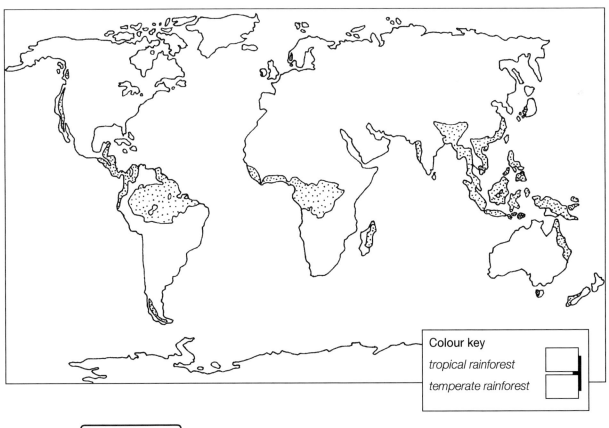

Colour key

*tropical rainforest* ☐

*temperate rainforest* ☐

**Fact file**

*Half of the world's rainforests lie within the borders of Brazil, Zaire and Indonesia.*

## Objectives

- *Reads information and answers questions about animals of the rainforest.*
- *Describes an imaginary rainforest animal with suitable adaptations.*

## Worksheet information

- Many of the world's rainforest animals are endangered. This is largely because of the destruction of their rainforest environment. Because some species only live in particular areas, the whole species can be killed when a large area of rainforest is cleared.
- There are more types of amphibians, birds, reptiles, insects and mammals living in rainforests than in any other environment.
- It is thought by scientists that up to 30 million species of tropical rainforest animals are yet to be discovered.
- The pupils may like to create poster-sized pictures or models of the imaginary rainforest animals they created on page 13.
- Quiz questions relating to this section may be found on page xi.

## Answers

### page 12

1. Teacher check
2. They are a food source for other animals and they carry pollen between plants, helping to fertilise them.
3. avoid predators – morpho butterfly, sloth, mandrill, coral snake

   eat/find food – aye-aye, tropical bettong, toucan

   catch prey – jaguar, aye-aye
4. Because it is the most likely place to find wood-boring grubs.
5. Teacher check

### page 13

Teacher check

## Cross-curricular activities

- In small groups, pupils research, create and record a 'soundscape' (a collection of sounds) that represents the animal sounds likely to be heard in a rainforest in a particular country.
- Organise an excursion to a zoo. Have the pupils write their observations of rainforest animals.
- Investigate the colours rainforest animals use for camouflage and scaring off predators. Why do the pupils think certain colours are used?

## Curriculum links

Page xix lists the main literacy and geography curriculum objectives covered by these activities. The final activity in this unit will help to teach the following curriculum objectives:

| England | English | KS 2 | • Use a range of writing forms. |
|---------|---------|------|--------------------------------|
| Northern Ireland | Language and literacy | KS 2 | • Use a variety of writing forms. |
| Republic of Ireland | English | 5th/6th Class | • Write in a wide variety of genres. |
| Scotland | English | Level C | • Write reports, based on reading. |
| Wales | English | KS 2 | • Write in a range of forms, in response to a wide range of stimuli. |

Rainforests provide a home to about half of the world's animals—and scientists believe there may also be millions of rainforest animal species that have yet to be discovered! Every layer of a rainforest has animals living in it, from the highest tree tops to the forest floor. Here are just a few examples of the insects, fish, birds, amphibians, mammals and reptiles you would find in rainforest areas around the world.

| | |
|---|---|
| **South America** | *morpho butterfly, jaguar, ocelot, piranha, toucan, coral snake, sloth* |
| **Australia** | *Boyd's forest dragon, tree kangaroo, green tree frog, tropical bettong* |
| **South-east Asia** | *gibbon, leafbird, Goliath birdwing butterfly, tiger, orang-outang* |
| **Africa** | *gorilla, hippopotamus, African grey parrot, aye-aye, mandrill* |

Insects are by far the commonest animal and have the greatest influence on the life of a rainforest; for example, they are a food source for many animals and they carry pollen between plants, helping to fertilise them.

Many rainforest animals are among the most unusual and beautiful in the world. Some are not found anywhere else; for example, the tree kangaroo is only found in Australian rainforests. Unfortunately, many rainforest animals have become endangered as their habitats continue to be destroyed by humans. Some of the rarer animals are also caught and sold illegally. It is alarming to learn that dozens of animal species become extinct every day in tropical rainforests.

Rainforest animals have developed some interesting adaptations to cope with living in their environment, including camouflage, behaviour, body colours or patterns and body parts.

---

### Camouflage
- The morpho butterfly's wings are electric blue on the upper side and dark on the underside. When the butterfly flutters along, the changing colours make it look as if it appears and then disappears.
- Rainforest cats like jaguars and ocelots have spots which make them hard to see in the shade of the canopy, allowing them to sneak up on their prey.

---

### Behaviour
- The aye-aye is a primate which likes to eat wood-boring grubs. It finds them by tapping on wood with its finger and listening for hollow spaces.
- The sloth is a mammal that moves so slowly it is difficult for its predators to see it.

---

### Body colours or patterns
- The mandrill is a large monkey from Africa. Its bright red and blue face scares away predators.
- The coral snake is highly venomous. Its yellow, red and black bands warn predators not to eat it. The kingsnake, which is not venomous, has similar markings to the coral snake, so predators leave it alone too!

---

### Body parts
- The tropical bettong is a small mammal that feeds mostly on fungi on the forest floor. It has developed a digestive system which can absorb nutrients from this unusual diet.
- The toucan has a strong beak which easily squashes the rainforest fruit it eats.

---

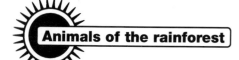
Use the text on page 11 to answer the questions.

1. Write a suitable question for each answer.

   (a) the gibbon _____

   _____

   (b) It has a bright red and blue face. _____

   _____

   (c) They are sold illegally. _____

   _____

   (d) It has similar markings to the coral snake. _____

   _____

2. Name two purposes rainforest insects have.

   (a) _____          (b) _____

   _____          _____

   _____          _____

3. Sort each animal into the category or categories that describe what its adaptations help it to do.

   jaguar
   mandrill
   tropical bettong
   coral snake
   morpho butterfly
   aye-aye
   toucan
   sloth

   | avoid predators | eat/find food | catch prey |
   |---|---|---|
   |  |  |  |

4. Why do you think the aye-aye listens for hollow spaces?

   _____

   _____

5. Which animal mentioned in the text would you most like to see? Explain.

   _____

   _____

   _____

   _____

**Fact file**

*If the current rate of rainforest destruction continues, approximately half of all mammals in peninsular Malaysia will become extinct by 2020.*

Scientists believe there may be millions of rainforest animals that have yet to be discovered. Imagine you are an explorer who has just found the most amazing rainforest animal. It is so well adapted to living in the rainforest, no wonder it was difficult to find!

1. Describe your animal below. You can use all or any of the animal adaptations described on page 11 or make up your own!

---

**Type of animal** ☐ insect ☐ fish ☐ bird ☐ amphibian ☐ mammal ☐ reptile

**Name of animal**

| |

**Country found**

| |

**Which part of the rainforest does it mostly live in? (e.g. tree tops, forest floor.)**

| |

**Does it have any predators? If so, name them. (They can be imaginary!)**

| |

**How does it move?**

| |

**What does it eat?**

| |

**What sound does it make?**

| |

### Adaptations

| Camouflage | Behaviour | Body colours/patterns | Body parts |
|---|---|---|---|
| | | | |

---

2. Draw and label a picture of your imaginary animal.

| |

**Fact file**

Tropical rainforests contain approximately 80% of all insect species.

## Objectives

- *Reads information and answers questions about animals of the rainforest.*
- *Plans and writes an animal myth using the typical features of traditional myths.*

## Worksheet information

- Myths are stories which explain a belief, practice or natural phenomenon and usually involve gods, demons or supernatural beings. A myth does not necessarily have a basis in fact or a natural explanation.
- Teachers will need to collect some traditional animal myths from different cultures to help the pupils complete page 17 (e.g. Rudyard Kipling's 'How the elephant got its trunk'). Time should be allowed for the pupils to read some of the myths and discuss them in small groups or as the class.
- Quiz questions relating to this section may be found on page xi.

## Answers

### page 16

1. (a) adult human, 12 cm
   (b) size of hand, 1.5 cm
   (c) shorter than giraffe, ruler length
2. The native rainforest people wipe their arrows or darts on the frog's skin to get the poison it secretes.
3. Teacher check
4.

| Animal | Place found | Eats | Physical features |
|--------|-------------|------|-------------------|
| Southern cassowary | New Guinea, Australia | fruit, fungi, frogs, snakes, flowers | about as tall as an adult human; long, glossy black feathers; blue and red colours on head/neck; brown, bony 'helmet'; long, sharp toenails |
| Poison arrow frog | South America | crickets, ants, flies, beetles | tiny, most are brightly coloured, poison secreted through skin |
| Okapi | Democratic Republic of Congo | grass, leaves, fruit, clay | shorter than a giraffe, reddish-brown body, head like a horse, zebra-like stripes on upper legs, long neck, long blue-black tongue |

5. Teacher check
6. Teacher check

### page 17

Teacher check

## Cross-curricular activities

- Research to find out how the okapi was discovered by western scientists.
- Find photographs of different poison arrow frogs. Use their patterns to make a variety of art works.

## Curriculum links

Page xix lists the main literacy and geography curriculum objectives covered by these activities. The final activity in this unit will help to teach the following curriculum objectives:

| England | English | KS 2 | • Use a range of writing forms, including narratives. |
|---------|---------|------|------------------------------------------------------|
| Northern Ireland | Language and literacy | KS 2 | • Use a variety of writing forms, including imaginative writing. |
| Republic of Ireland | English | 5th/6th Class | • Write in a wide variety of genres, including narratives. |
| Scotland | English | Level C | • Develop imaginative writing. |
| Wales | English | KS 2 | • Write in a range of forms, in response to a wide range of stimuli, including imaginative writing. |

## Southern cassowary

The southern cassowary is a flightless bird that lives in the rainforests of Australia and New Guinea. Shy and solitary, it is the third largest bird in the world after the ostrich and the emu.

It would be difficult to mistake the cassowary for any other bird. Not only is it about as tall as an adult human, it has long, glossy black feathers and bright blue and red colours on its head and neck. It also has a brown, bony 'helmet' on its head, which prevents leaves and twigs from poking into its eyes when it is moving through the forest. The cassowary has sharp toenails that it can use to defend itself. These can grow to 12 centimetres in length! Cassowaries have been known to attack humans by kicking with their legs, although this is rare.

Southern cassowaries mostly eat fruit but they will also eat other things like fungi, frogs, snakes and flowers. Cassowary dung often contains whole fruit seeds, which can germinate and grow into new plants.

Unfortunately, the southern cassowary is endangered. This is due to its rainforest habitat being cleared for housing, dog attacks and being hit by cars.

## Poison arrow frog

The poison arrow frog lives in the rainforests of South America. There are many different species, most of which are brightly coloured. Poison arrow frogs are tiny. The largest species is about the size of your hand and the smallest species only grows to about 1.5 cm! Due to their size, poison arrow frogs eat small insects like crickets, ants, flies and beetles.

These frogs get their interesting name from the poison they secrete through their skin. The native rainforest people wipe their arrows or darts onto the frog's skin, supplying them with a powerful deadly poison which can kill animals quickly. In fact, the poison in just one frog is capable of killing up to 100 humans!

Female poison arrow frogs lay their eggs in or near water. When the tadpoles hatch, either the male or the female frog (depending on the species) will carry them on his/her back to a small, safe pool of water, where they can develop into frogs.

## Okapi

The okapi is the only known living relative of the giraffe. It lives in the rainforest of the Democratic Republic of Congo in Africa. This amazing-looking animal is shorter than the giraffe, with a reddish-brown body, a head like a horse, zebra-like stripes on its upper legs and a long neck. It also has a blue-black tongue that is about the length of a ruler!

The okapi lives alone or in small groups, roaming for grass, leaves and fruit to eat, as well as clay from river banks, which provides it with the minerals its body needs. The okapi's main predator is the leopard.

It wasn't until 1901 that the okapi was discovered by western scientists, although African people from the area in which it is found were aware of its existence a long time before this.

Use the text on page 15 to answer the questions.

1. Complete the size facts for each animal.

   (a) cassowary          height _____          toenail length _____

   (b) poison arrow frog  largest _____          smallest _____

   (c) okapi              height _____          tongue length _____

2. How did the poison arrow frog get its name?

   _____

   _____

3. Which animal would you least like to come into contact with? _____

   Explain. _____

   _____

   _____

4. Complete the table.

| Animal | Place found | Eats | Physical features |
|--------|-------------|------|-------------------|
| Southern cassowary | | | |
| Poison arrow frog | | | |
| Okapi | | | |

5. What could Australians do to help the endangered cassowary?

   _____

   _____

6. List some possible reasons why it might have taken so long for the okapi to have been discovered by western scientists.

**Fact file**

*The poisons secreted by poison arrow frogs may be beneficial as muscle relaxants in humans — in very small quantities.*

*Many cultures have myths that explain why animals do certain things or look a particular way.*

*Follow the steps below to help you write your own myth about one of the animals described on page 15. Your myth could explain how the animal gained one or more of its physical features, why it behaves in certain ways, what it eats or why it has certain enemies.*

1. Read some animal myths from different cultures.

   (a) Write some of the titles. _____

   _____

   _____

   (b) List some of the things these myths have in common.
       You could consider the types of characters and the plot.

2. Choose one of the rainforest animals from page 15. Brainstorm and then list some possible titles for a myth about it. Circle the one you like the best.

   **Animal**                    **Title ideas**

3. Plan your myth in the space below.

   | **Beginning:** |
   |---|
   | **Middle:** |
   | **End:** |

4. Write your myth on a separate sheet of paper. Read it aloud to a small group.

   **Fact file**
   *The okapi can use its tongue to clean out its ears!*

# Big butterflies, scary snakes and magnificent monkeys

## Objectives

- *Reads information and answers questions about animals of the rainforest.*
- *Plans and conducts an interview with a partner.*

## Worksheet information

- Teachers may like to record the pupils' interviews (page 21) with a video camera. The interviews could form part of a rainforest television programme, with the pupils adding other interviews, reports, a weather segment etc.
- Quiz questions relating to this section may be found on page xii.

## Answers

### page 20

Some answers may include:

1. Both are threatened by rainforest destruction, have been hunted by humans, don't often come to the ground, eat flowers (the Queen Alexandra's birdwing butterfly eats the nectar) and leaves.

2. (a) true

   (b) false

   (c) false

   (d) true

3. It uses tree branches as springboards.

4. Teacher check

5.

| Animal | Foods |
|---|---|
| Queen Alexandra's birdwing butterfly | pipe vine leaves (caterpillar), nectar |
| Anaconda | deer, tapirs, birds, aquatic animals like turtles and fish |
| Colobus monkey | leaves, flowers, fruit, insects |

### page 21

Teacher check

## Cross-curricular activities

- Research to create a collection of rainforest animal 'records'; e.g. biggest insect, loudest monkey, longest snake.
- Make educational posters that encourage people to leave anacondas alone.

## Curriculum links

Page xix lists the main literacy and geography curriculum objectives covered by these activities. The final activity in this unit will help to teach the following curriculum objectives:

| England | English | KS 2 | • Work in role and gain and maintain the interest of different audiences. |
|---|---|---|---|
| Northern Ireland | Language and literacy | KS 2 | • Prepare questionnaires to seek information and improvise a scene based on curricular topics. |
| Republic of Ireland | English | 5th/6th Class | • Practise and use improvisational drama. |
| Scotland | English | Level C | • Select questions appropriate to the purpose of an interview, showing an awareness of listener's needs. |
| Wales | English | KS 2 | • Participate in a range of drama activities and present and perform, live and on tape. |

## Queen Alexandra's birdwing butterfly

The Queen Alexandra's birdwing butterfly lives in a small area of rainforest in New Guinea. It is the largest butterfly in the world. The wingspan of the female butterfly can be up to 30 centimetres long—the length of a ruler! The male butterfly is smaller and looks quite different. It has black wings with yellow, blue, green and red markings, while the female has dark brown wings with cream and red markings.

The female butterfly only lays its eggs on one type of plant—the pipe vine. The caterpillars that hatch from the eggs eat the leaves, then make cocoons and change into butterflies. Like all butterflies, they have a short life span—only about three months.

Queen Alexandra's birdwing butterflies don't often come to the ground. They like to fly high in the air where they feed on the nectar of flowers. This can make it difficult to find out how many there are, but it is known that they are endangered. This is mainly because large areas of their rainforest home have been cleared of trees. Some people also catch and sell them illegally.

## Anaconda

The anaconda is a gigantic, non-poisonous snake found in South American rainforests. It can grow to about nine metres in length and 30 centimetres in diameter.

Anacondas are solitary animals that prefer to live in or near water. Their eyes and nostrils are on top of their heads, allowing them to breathe and see their prey while the rest of their body remains hidden underwater. When an animal like a deer, tapir or bird approaches the water's edge, the anaconda strikes, grabbing the animal with its sharp teeth and pulling it underwater. The prey then either drowns or is crushed to death by the anaconda's strong body. Anacondas also catch and eat aquatic creatures like turtles and fish. Whatever the prey, it is always eaten whole. If the prey is bigger than the anaconda, it simply unhinges its jaw to increase the size of its mouth. After eating a large animal, an anaconda may not eat again for weeks.

Although few humans have been attacked by anacondas, many people will kill one when they see it, out of fear for their lives. This is the greatest threat to the snake's existence, followed closely by the destruction of its rainforest habitat.

## Colobus monkey

The colobus monkey is found in East African rainforests. Once hunted for its beautiful black and white fur, its greatest threat today is rainforest destruction by humans.

Unlike most other monkeys, the colobus doesn't have a thumb. This helps it to travel swiftly along tree branches. It also uses branches like springboards to leap from tree to tree. A colobus monkey can spring up to 15 metres high, using its white fur 'mantle' and its long tail like a parachute for its descents. It spends almost all of its life in the treetops, rarely coming to the ground.

Colobus monkeys live in troops of up to 25. The members of a troop mark their home range by making croaking and rattling sounds in their throats. The troop spends its mornings and evenings searching for food—especially leaves. One monkey can eat two kilograms of leaves in a day! The colobus also eat other food like flowers and fruit and the occasional insect.

Use the text on page 19 to answer the questions.

1. List similarities between the Queen Alexandra's birdwing butterfly and the colobus monkey.

2. Tick 'true' or 'false'.

   True ◯ False ◯ (a) An anaconda can eat prey larger than itself.

   True ◯ False ◯ (b) The male and female Queen Alexandra's birdwing butterflies are identical.

   True ◯ False ◯ (c) Colobus monkeys live on their own.

   True ◯ False ◯ (d) The Queen Alexandra's birdwing butterfly's wingspan can be up to the length of a ruler.

3. How does the colobus monkey manage to spring so high in the air?

   _____

   _____

4. Give your opinion on each of these issues.

   (a) People catching and selling the Queen Alexandra's birdwing butterfly.

   _____

   _____

   (b) People killing anacondas. _____

   _____

   (c) People hunting the colobus monkey for its fur. _____

   _____

5. Complete the table with the foods that each of these animals eats.

| Animal | Foods |
|---|---|
| Queen Alexandra's birdwing butterfly | |
| Anaconda | |
| Colobus monkey | |

**Fact file**

*The name 'colobus' comes from a Greek word meaning 'mutilated'.*
*This refers to the colobus monkey's lack of a thumb.*

*Imagine you have the ability to talk to animals. You decide to interview one of the rainforest animals described on page 19 about its life.*

1. Which animal would you most like to interview? _____

2. Circle the three interview questions from the list below you would most like to ask this animal.

   - What do you think of human beings?

   - What is your favourite food? Why do you like it?

   - Do you like living in a rainforest? Why/Why not?

   - What are some of your favourite things to do?

   - What makes you special?

   - If you could have one wish, what would it be?

3. Write three more interview questions of your own.

   - _____

   - _____

   - _____

4. Find a partner who has chosen the same animal as you. Choose the six interview questions you like the best.

5. With your partner, write what you think this animal would be like to interview. What sort of personality do you think it would have? How would it move and talk?

| *Personality* | *Movement/Speech* |
|---|---|
| | |

6. Decide who will be the interviewer and who will be the animal. Practise your interview with your partner, using your six favourite questions and your ideas from Question 5.

7. Present your interview to the class.

**Fact file**

*Butterfly farms are run in New Guinea to provide income and help save endangered butterflies like the Queen Alexandra's birdwing.*

## Objectives

- *Reads information and answers questions about plants of the rainforest.*
- *Researches to find information to complete detailed sketches of plants and animals of the rainforest.*

## Worksheet information

- Tropical rainforests cover about 6% of the Earth's surface, which is why they are so important to the Earth's ecosystem.
- Products from tropical rainforest plants are used to make rugs, mattresses, rope, string, fabrics and industrial processes. Oils, gums and resins from plants are used in insecticides, rubber products, fuel, paint, varnish and wood finishing products, cosmetics, soaps, disinfectants and detergents. Timbers such as teak, mahogany, rosewood, balsa and sandalwood all come from tropical rainforests and are highly prized.
- A drug called Vincristine, made from a rainforest plant, periwinkle, is one of the world's most potent anticancer drugs. It has dramatically increased the incidence of survival for children with acute leukaemia.
- Page 25 may be enlarged to A3 size to allow pupils to complete more detailed sketches.
- Quiz questions relating to this section may be found on page xii.

## Answers

### page 24

1. (a) (iv) two-thirds

   (b) (iii) because the conditions are hot and wet

   (c) (i) potatoes, marrows and yams; (ii) cayenne, black pepper, cloves (iii) oranges, lemons, grapefruit

   (d) Pupils should underline ALL answers.

2. Teacher check

### page 25

Teacher check

## Cross-curricular activities

- Pupils design a menu for a meal incorporating an appetiser, main course and dessert, using food from the tropical rainforest; for example, potato and corn soup (appetiser); spicy fish with peppers, potatoes, yams and beans (main course); tropical fruit salad with coconut vanilla cream (dessert). Pupils may also mention a coffee or chocolate drink to conclude the meal. Pupils select one course to make for a 'tropical rainforest' feast.
- Pupils collect an empty soft drink bottle to use to contain a mini-rainforest. Pupils use various types of plants to create the four layers of the rainforest.
- In groups of four, eight or twelve, pupils listen to appropriate music and use their bodies to typify various plants growing and surviving in the different layers of the rainforest.

## Curriculum links

Page xix lists the main literacy and geography curriculum objectives covered by these activities. The final activity in this unit will help to teach the following curriculum objectives:

| England | Art and design | KS 2 | • Record from first-hand observation. |
|---|---|---|---|
| Northern Ireland | Art | KS 2 | • Investigate and respond to reference materials through drawing. |
| Republic of Ireland | Visual arts | 5th/6th Class | • Draw from observation, based on themes. |
| Scotland | Art and design | Level C | • Explore a range of drawing techniques and record natural objects. |
| Wales | Art | KS 2 | • Make images in two dimensions, using various materials. |

The rainforests are home to a huge variety of plant and animal life. More than two-thirds of the world's plant species can be found in tropical rainforests.

Plants grow very well in the rainforest because the conditions are hot and wet, similar to a greenhouse. Some of the tallest trees in the world grow in tropical rainforests. Other plants adapt their roots, trunks, bark and leaves to suit the conditions.

At least 80% of the developed world's diet originated from plants in the tropical rainforest. This includes avocados, citrus and tropical fruits, tomatoes, vegetables, spices, chocolate, coffee, vanilla, coconuts, nuts and cashews.

Plants are vital to the ecology of our planet, since they generate much of the Earth's oxygen. They store carbon dioxide in their roots, stems, branches and leaves and convert it to oxygen for clean air.

Ingredients, such as alkaloids, can be obtained from rainforest plants to use in medicines; 25% of Western drugs are made from ingredients derived from rainforest plants.

Plants from the rainforest also provide rubber for tyres, materials for baskets and rope and chemicals to make perfumes, soaps, polishes and chewing gum.

The plants of the rainforest grow to form distinct layers. There are four main layers. These are:

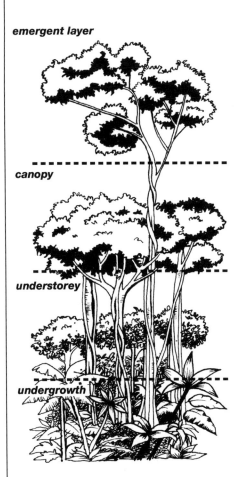

emergent layer

canopy

understorey

undergrowth

***Emergent layer***, which is the tallest layer and only found in tropical rainforests. It usually consists of the tops of trees which are over 45 metres tall. Many birds, butterflies, small monkeys, bats, snakes and insects live in this layer.

***Canopy layer***, which consists mainly of trees between 25 to 35 metres tall. This layer covers and protects the layers below. It stops a lot of light from penetrating to the lower layers and helps prevent soil erosion from heavy rains. A few of these trees may push through to become part of the emergent layer. Birds, monkeys, frogs, sloth, snakes and many lizards live in the canopy.

***Understorey layer***, which consists of smaller trees, shrubs or trees which have not reached the canopy layer. Once a gap appears, these trees are able to push through. Trees in this layer are usually small with thin trunks and grow about 20 metres tall. The understorey is a cool, dark environment suitable for birds, butterflies, frogs and snakes.

***Undergrowth layer*** is sometimes divided into two sub-layers — a *shrub layer* and the *forest floor*. The shrub layer is made up of ferns and small shrubs. The forest floor is the darkest layer of a rainforest due to the fact that the trees above prevent the light from penetrating. A layer of leaves, twigs and dead plants cover the soil of the forest floor. These rot down quickly to provide nutrients for the plants. Mosses and ferns grow in this layer. Most of the animal life lives in the undergrowth layer, including tigers, elephants, gorillas, leopards, tapirs, jaguars and insects.

# Plants of the rainforest – 2

Use the text on page 23 to answer the questions.

1. Underline the correct answers.

   (a) What fraction of the world's plants can be found in tropical rainforests?
   - (i) one-quarter
   - (ii) one-third
   - (iii) three-quarters
   - (iv) two-thirds
   - (v) half

   (b) Why do plants grow so well in the tropical rainforest?
   - (i) because they get lots of light
   - (ii) because the soil is very rich
   - (iii) because the conditions are hot and wet

   (c) Which foods originated in the rainforest?
   - (i) potatoes, marrows and yams
   - (ii) cayenne, black pepper, cloves
   - (iii) oranges, lemons, grapefruit
   - (iv) prawns and lobster

   (d) What are some other reasons for the importance of rainforest plants?
   - (i) they generate clean air for the Earth
   - (ii) they provide ingredients for lifesaving drugs
   - (iii) they provide rubber for tyres
   - (iv) they provide materials for baskets and rope
   - (v) they provide chemicals for perfumes, soaps, polishes and chewing gum

2. Use brief bullet points to complete the table.

| Layer | Types of plants | Types of animals | Other interesting facts |
|---|---|---|---|
| emergent | | | |
| canopy | | | |
| understorey | | | |
| undergrowth | | | |

**Fact file**

The Indians of the rainforest use over 2000 of the 3000 types of fruit which can be found in the rainforest.

1. Use library or Internet resources to find an illustration of the layers of the rainforest. Use the box to lightly sketch the various layers of the rainforest. Label the layers and then colour your sketch with a variety of green crayons, pencils or markers.

*emergent layer*

*canopy*

*understorey*

*undergrowth*

2. Sketch one or two birds or animals next to each layer to show where they belong. You may need to research library or Internet resources to find information about specific animals for each layer. Draw them as realistically as possible and use the correct colours.

**Fact file**

*In one square kilometre of rainforest, as many as 300 different species of tree may be found.*

## Objectives

- *Reads information and answers questions about specific plants of the rainforest.*
- *Follows a procedure to create a 'mini'-rainforest.*

## Worksheet information

- The plants chosen for this section are tropical rainforest plants. Many other plants not mentioned are also found in temperate rainforests. These include evergreen conifers such as spruce, maple trees, cottonwood, alder, fir, Western red cedar and giant eucalyptus.
- Quiz questions relating to this section may be found on page xiii.

## Answers

### page 28

1.  (a) ... the roots, trunk, bark and leaves of many trees have adapted to suit the hot, wet conditions in which they live.
    (b) ... some rather strange and unusual plant life.
2.  (a) buttress/stilt/prop roots or saprophytes
    (b) buttress/stilt/prop roots or lianas
    (c) saprophytes
    (d) lianas/epiphytes
    (e) lianas
    (f) lianas (suckers or tendrils)
    (g) epiphytes
    (h) epiphytes
3.  Teacher check

### page 29

Teacher check

## Cross-curricular activities

- Pupils care for a selection of indoor plants in the classroom. Aspects such as water, nutrients and light requirements for particular plants should be thoroughly researched and applied for optimum growth.
- Pupils create wordsearches or crossword puzzles using vocabulary from the informational text on page 27.
- Pupils plant quick-growing seeds such as sunflower or bean seeds and plot their growth or rate of growth on a chart over a given time, noting periods of accelerated growth and periods of slower growth. Pupils suggest reasons for differing degrees of growth.

## Curriculum links

Page xix lists the main literacy and geography curriculum objectives covered by these activities. The final activity in this unit will help to teach the following curriculum objectives:

| England | English | KS 2 | • Read a range of non-fiction texts. |
| --- | --- | --- | --- |
| Northern Ireland | Language and literacy | KS 2 | • Engage in a wide range of reading activities for a variety of purposes. |
| Republic of Ireland | English | 5th/6th Class | • Read and interpret different kinds of functional text. |
| Scotland | English | Level C/D | • Use reading in group activities and complete practical reading tasks. |
| Wales | English | KS 2 | • Read and use a wide range of sources of information and read for different purposes. |

# Plant profiles - 1 | Plants of the rainforest

The trees and plants that grow in the tropical rainforest are special. The roots, trunks, bark and leaves of many trees have adapted to suit the hot, wet conditions in which they live. Many of these adaptations have resulted in some rather strange and unusual plant life!

1. The soil in a tropical rainforest may be very thin and poor with all the nutrients just on the surface. As a result, tall rainforest trees usually have shallow root systems which do not provide the tree with very much support. Often trees develop a system of flared roots known as **buttress roots**.

   These may spread away from the trunk across the forest floor in all directions for up to one hundred feet or more. One example of this is the Ceiba tree.

   Other trees may develop **stilt** or **prop** roots which are aerial 'fingers' which extend from the trunk and fork down into the soil to anchor the tree. Mangrove forest trees survive in this manner.

2. **Lianas** are thick, woody vines which climb up and around trees to reach the sunlight coming through. They have their roots firmly planted in the ground but are able to spread from tree to tree (over 900 metres). They use sucker roots or tendrils to support themselves on the trees. When lianas reach the top of the canopy, they can tangle around other lianas to form a network of vines.

   This gives shallow-rooted, top-heavy trees extra support against strong winds. The philodendron is one example of a liana.

3. **Epiphytes** (air plants) grow on other plants to get to the sun. They attach themselves to the branches, trunks, stems, leaves and branches of other plants. Their roots do not grow into the 'host' plant so they do not use it for water or nutrients. Instead, they derive their water and nutrients from the rain. Epiphytes such as ferns, orchids and bromeliads, produce their own food in their leaves. Epiphytes may need adaptations such as aerial roots (to absorb water from the air), swollen stems (to store water), water tanks (to funnel water) or dead leaves (to form a sponge at the roots). Many epiphytes are reproduced by spores or seeds deposited in the canopy by birds or the wind.

4. **Saprophytes** are the organisms which grow on dead and decaying plants and animals. As leaves, branches and dead animals fall to the forest floor, saprophytes break down the nutrients in them to help feed other living things. Because it is so hot and wet in the tropical rainforest this decomposition can happen as quickly as 24 hours. Fungi and bacteria belong to this group. Some saprophytes such as microbes are too small to be seen with the naked eye.

Use the text on page 27 to answer the questions.

1. Complete the sentences using words directly from the text.

   (a) The trees and plants that grow in the tropical rainforest are special because

   _____

   _____

   (b) Many plant adaptations have resulted in _____

   _____

2. Choose the correct adaptation from the list which may provide a solution to the problem shown. (Hint: There may be more than one.)

   | • *buttress, stilt or prop roots*    • *saprophytes*    • *lianas*    • *epiphytes* |
   | --- |

   (a) thin, poor soil

   _____

   (b) tall, thin tree trunks

   _____

   (c) dead animals and decaying plants on the forest floor

   _____

   (d) unable to reach sunlight

   _____

   (e) shallow tree roots with a top-heavy canopy of leaves

   _____

   (f) no viable trunk to support growth

   _____

   (g) inability to grow independently

   _____

   (h) cannot use roots to get nutrients

   _____

3. Use some of the adaptations mentioned to create a 'new' plant which will survive in the tropical rainforest and match the description below. Draw and label your plant.

   'This tropical plant survives in very poor light and must compete with the larger plants for water and nutrients. It has unusual flowers and leaves which aid its survival. It grows independently of other plants and, although it has a short life span, is able to produce vast numbers of seeds which ensure its survival.'

   **Fact file**

   *It takes 60 years for a tropical rainforest tree to grow big enough to be used for timber.*

*Follow the procedure below to create your own rainforest in a bottle. Tick each step as you complete it.*

## Materials

- *a large, clean, clear, plastic soft drink or juice container with the cap still on*
- *very sharp scissors or a craft knife (use with care)*
- *soil or potting mix*
- *small plants of various heights to represent the different layers of the rainforest (vines, ground cover plants or low spreading plants are suitable for the forest floor). One or two plants of each height will be sufficient!*
- *gardening gloves/plastic gloves (Potting mix may contain harmful organisms!)*
- *water*

## Method

- Separate the top from the bottom of the bottle using the scissors or craft knife so that you have two sections. (The bottom section will be used to plant the layers into and the top with the lid on it will go over to form a cover.) ☐
- Use the bottom of the drink bottle as a scoop and fill it with potting mix. ☐
- Plant the tallest plants (emergent) first in the potting mix, followed by those for the canopy, then the undergrowth plants and finally the forest floor ground cover plants or vines. ☐
- Add small twigs, dead leaves or rocks. ☐
- Moisten the plants gently with water. Be sure not to 'flood' them! ☐
- Cover the base with the clear top of the bottle. ☐
- Place in a well-lit position — not direct sun! ☐

## Evaluation

1. How easy was the procedure to follow? **Easy** ☐ **Okay** ☐ **Hard** ☐

2. Were any steps more difficult to follow than others? If so, which ones and why? _____

   _____

3. Rate your completed terrarium. (1 – Poor; 5 – Great!)  ① ② ③ ④ ⑤

---

**Fact file**

*The pitcher plant is a carnivorous plant which grows up to 9 m tall. It may have pitchers 30 cm in length full of digested insects. It can also eat small mammals and reptiles.*

## People of the rainforest

People of the rainforest

### Objectives

- *Reads information and answers questions about people of the rainforest.*
- *Designs and constructs a model of a typical rainforest home.*

### Worksheet information

- There are many groups, each with their own language and culture, living in the world's rainforests today. These indigenous people have lived in the rainforests for thousands of years, learning about their environment and passing this knowledge from one generation to the next. Everything they require for survival comes from the forest. They live a sustainable existence, protecting their environment from damage.
- A sustainable farming method known as shifting or slash and burn is practised by many indigenous people. A small area of land is cleared and then burned. Plants for food and medicine are cultivated. After some time, another area is prepared for cultivation while this land is left fallow to regenerate.
- The rapid destruction of the rainforests is affecting the livelihood of many of these indigenous people. They are being left with less land to cultivate, resulting in overuse of the soil, which is eventually stripped of all its nutrients.
- Pupils may collect resources such as twigs, leaves and grass from the playground to construct their models on page 33.
- Quiz questions relating to this section may be found on page xiii.

### Answers

**page 32**

1. (a) Traditional life in the rainforest is very primitive.
   (b) Speaking several tribal languages is useful for trading purposes.
   (c) Gas and electricity are unavailable in rainforest areas.
   (d) Everyone has a role to play in village life.
2. Teacher check

3. Tropical rainforests are located close to the equator where it is hot all year round.
4. & 5. Teacher check

**page 33**
Teacher check

### Cross-curricular activities

- Research to compile a list of every step that has to be taken before the meat from an animal killed on a hunting trip can be eaten. Present the list as an illustrated booklet.
- Research and find data to compare the annual temperature and humidity of a tropical and a temperate rainforest area with the pupils' own area. Graph the data and explain what it shows. Pupils consider which climate they would prefer and why.
- Research the reasons why areas of rainforest are being destroyed and at what rate. Pupils take on different roles and present their arguments; e.g. conservationists, indigenous people, logging and mining companies.

### Curriculum links

Page xix lists the main literacy and geography curriculum objectives covered by these activities. The final activity in this unit will help to teach the following curriculum objectives:

| England | Design and technology | KS 2 | • Complete design and make assignments, reflect on their work and identify improvements. |
|---------|----------------------|------|--------------------------------------------------|
| Northern Ireland | Science and technology | KS 2 | • Develop competence with tools and techniques when designing and making objects or models. |
| Republic of Ireland | Science | 5th/6th Class | • Present a design proposal, make objects and appraise results. |
| Scotland | Technology | Level C | • Communicate a design plan and evaluate their work. |
| Wales | Design and technology | KS 2 | • Design and make products and evaluate their work. |

Millions of people have their homes in the world's rainforests. For some tropical rainforest people, their lives have changed very little for many generations. They use their environment for all their needs, from food and shelter to medicine and recreation. The homes of many rainforest tribes are very isolated and great distances from the nearest towns. There are no telephones deep in the rainforest, limiting contact with the outside world. Many people never travel to the cities, where they would encounter a very different way of life. The greatest threat to their ancient lifestyles is the destruction of the rainforests by developers and industrial companies.

People of the rainforest move around mostly on foot. To travel down a river, the men make canoes, dug out from large tree trunks. Villages trade with one another and some have contact with the towns and cities. It is possible that a typical rainforest home may have some modern, machine-made items such as metal pots and pans, plastic containers, decorations and clothes.

Many people within a tribe only speak their own language, but some also speak the languages of other tribes and villages. This is very important for trade. Those who have contact with the towns and cities also speak the national language of their country.

For many, many years, the people of the rainforests have known the medicinal value of many species of plants and animals. Each community has a medicine man or shaman who passes his knowledge to the next generation.

Traditionally, the men are the hunters who use their handmade weapons to kill their prey and provide food for the community. Boys are taught the skills of hunting very early, learning how to recognise the signs of different

animals and to follow them closely without scaring them away. They learn how to fish skilfully using long spears.

The women look after the home, caring for the children, preparing the food and making pots and baskets for storage containers. Everyone has a job to do. Even the very young children collect firewood and fruit, recognising which is edible and safe to eat. There is no gas or electricity in the rainforests. Food is cooked over an open fire, surrounded with stones to maintain the heat.

It rains a lot in the rainforest so shelters need to be waterproof. Thick thatched roofs, supported by large poles cut from trees, keep the rain out and building the floors above ground level stops everything from getting wet when the ground is soaked with rain. Some tropical rainforest homes have no walls as it is never cold.

In some areas of the rainforests, people have set up schools where the children learn to read and write. Even those who do not go to school are learning things every day, important skills to help them survive in the rainforest environment.

There is also time for fun. Children enjoy swimming in the rivers, playing with handmade toys and taking part in other fun activities, just like children all over the world.

**People of the rainforest - 2**

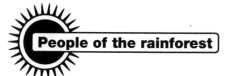

Use the text on page 31 to answer the questions.

1. Match the beginning of each sentence to its end.

(a) Traditional life in the rainforest •          • unavailable in rainforest areas.

(b) Speaking many tribal languages is •          • a role to play in village life.

(c) Gas and electricity are •          • is very primitive.

(d) Everyone has •          • useful for trading purposes.

2. List three things you might have to do in a rainforest community in single day if you were:

(a) a man

_____

_____

_____

(b) a woman

_____

_____

_____

(c) a child

_____

_____

_____

3. Why is it never cold in tropical rainforests?

_____

_____

_____

4. (a) Do you think people of the rainforest have a healthy lifestyle?

Yes◯ No◯

(b) Give reasons for your answer.

```
┌─────────────────────────────────┐
│                                 │
│                                 │
│                                 │
│                                 │
└─────────────────────────────────┘
```

5. (a) Would you like to spend a week in a rainforest village? Yes◯ No◯

(b) List the things you think you would enjoy.

_____

_____

_____

(c) List the things you would miss about home.

_____

_____

_____

**Fact file**

*There are at least 3000 different edible fruits to be found in the rainforests.*

1. Construct a typical rainforest home.

   (a) Design and sketch your home, labelling each section.

   (b) List the materials you will use to build your rainforest home.

2. Build your home, listing the steps you took to build it.

3. How could you improve your construction?

4. Mark the line to indicate the success of your construction.

   $(1)$ $(2)$ $(3)$ $(4)$ $(5)$ $(6)$ $(7)$ $(8)$ $(9)$ $(10)$

   **POOR**      **REASONABLE**      **EXCELLENT**

**Fact file**

*Less than 1% of tropical rainforest plants have been tested for their medicinal value by major pharmaceutical companies, yet over 25% of all ingredients for modern medicines were originally found in tropical rainforests.*

## People of the rainforest

# Traditional rainforest tribes

## Objectives

- *Reads information and answers questions about traditional rainforest tribes.*
- *Designs and constructs a musical instrument from recyclable materials.*

## Worksheet information

- Indigenous people have lived in the world's rainforests for thousands of years. Their lives began to change with the arrival of early European explorers, over 500 years ago. Explorers brought with them diseases to which the rainforest people had no immunity, drastically reducing their numbers. Some tribes have disappeared altogether. With the exploitation and destruction of the rainforests the numbers are decreasing even further.

- Although many people live as we do, some still follow the lives and traditions of their ancestors. All their needs are met by the resources found in the forests.

- People of the rainforest use their environment sustainably, taking only what they need and limiting any damage they might make in the process. They have a great respect for the forests as they provide them with everything they need to maintain their lifestyles.

- Pupils should select resources for constructing their musical instrument such as small hollow branches, large cardboard rolls, ice-cream containers, margarine containers etc.

- Quiz questions relating to this section may be found on page xiv.

## Answers

### page 36

1. Huli – New Guinea, Yanomami – Brazil, Mbuti – Central Africa.
2. 2– 6. Teacher check

### page 37

Teacher check

## Cross-curricular activities

- Research tribes who live in different parts of the world's rainforests. Compare the similarities and differences in their lifestyles. Present information in a Venn diagram. Use the diagram as an aid to present a talk on the subject.

- Employ a range of art and design technology techniques to make traditional artefacts used by people of the rainforests.

- Choose a rainforest tribe and present a project on their history, lifestyle, celebrations and traditions and how the destruction of the rainforests is affecting them.

## Curriculum links

Page xix lists the main literacy and geography curriculum objectives covered by these activities. The final activity in this unit will help to teach the following curriculum objectives:

| England | Design and technology | KS 2 | • Complete design and make assignments, reflect on their work and identify improvements. |
| Northern Ireland | Science and technology | KS 2 | • Develop competence with tools and techniques when designing and making models which incorporate sound. |
| Republic of Ireland | Science | 5th/6th Class | • Present a design proposal, make objects and appraise results. |
| Scotland | Technology | Level C | • Communicate a design plan and evaluate their work. |
| Wales | Design and technology | KS 2 | • Design and make products and evaluate their work. |

People who live in temperate rainforests generally have access to all the conveniences of the modern technological era. But in the tropical rainforests there are many indigenous people who live much as their ancestors have done for many years. Most are hunter-gatherers or subsistence farmers. This means they grow and hunt only to meet their immediate needs. They practise the slash and burn method of preparing land for farming. First they clear a piece of land, then burn the remaining stubble. This releases many nutrients into the soil, making the soil richer for farming. This land is cultivated for a while but before it is totally stripped of goodness, another area is prepared and used.

To these people, the traditional methods of living and celebrating their lives and cultures are very important and the destruction of the forests by large organisations is threatening this way of life.

The Yanomami tribe live in the Amazon rainforest in Brazil. The whole village lives in a yano, a huge communal house. A yano is a round building, made with vine and leaf thatch. Each family has space in the covered area and the open centre is for communal activities. The hunters in the tribe never eat meat from an animal they have caught. Instead, they share it with others and, in return, receive meat caught by someone else.

The Tukano tribe also live in the Amazon rainforests of Brazil. Even though they are small people, they are very strong. One of their traditions is that men are always named after birds and women after plants. The Mbuti are a pygmy tribe of hunter-gatherers who live in Central Africa. Pygmies are very short, less than 150 cm tall. For them, the forest is the centre of the world. Everything they require can be found in the forest and they treat it with respect, taking only what they need.

Like all rainforest people, the Mbuti are very knowledgeable about the edible plants and animals in the forest. Food sources include mushrooms, termites and honey. They are led to the beehives by the Greater Honeyguide bird which lives on beeswax.

One of the Mbuti tribe's traditions is the molimo. This is a sacred ritual of either celebration, giving thanks to the forest for what it provides, or a method of returning calm to the community after an event such as a death. The molimo is also the name of the trumpet-like instrument through which the men sing to make beautiful music and animal noises, both of which are part of the ritual. This ritual is made sacred by the Mbuti's beliefs in the goodness of the forest.

The Huli tribe live in the highlands of New Guinea. For ceremonies, the men wear elaborate headdresses and decorate their bodies with coloured clay. The Huli live mainly on a diet of yams, manioc (a starchy plant root) and, occasionally, meat from domestic pigs or forest animals such as cassowaries or tree kangaroos.

Use the text on page 35 to answer the questions.

1. Match each tribe to its correct location.

| | | | |
|---|---|---|---|
| Huli | • | • | Central Africa |
| Yanomami | • | • | New Guinea |
| Mbuti | • | • | Brazil |

2. What does the term *hunter-gatherer* mean?

_____

_____

_____

_____

3. (a) Write two advantages of living in a close community such as the Yanomami tribe.

_____

_____

_____

_____

(b) Write two disadvantages of living in a close community.

_____

_____

_____

_____

4. How is the destruction of the rainforests affecting the lives of the people there?

_____

_____

_____

_____

_____

_____

_____

_____

5. How do the rainforest people know so much about their environment when they do not have access to libraries and the Internet?

_____

_____

_____

_____

_____

_____

6. What traditions do you celebrate in your community? Give the name of and reason for one tradition.

_____

_____

_____

_____

_____

_____

**Fact file**

*Until 1950, no-one in the western world knew of the existence of the Yanomami tribe.*

*Many indigenous rainforest people make musical instruments using local resources.*

1.  Design and make a musical instrument from resources you already have.

    (a) Sketch the instrument.

    (b) Make a list of materials required.

    _____

    _____

    _____

    _____

    (c) Explain how the instrument is to be constructed.

    _____

    _____

    _____

    _____

    _____

    (d) How is the instrument to be played?

    _____

    _____

    _____

    _____

2.  Build your instrument. How successful is it? Tick 'yes' or 'no'.

    (a) Does it play different notes?
       Yes  No

    (b) Can a tune be played on it?
       Yes  No

    (c) Is it durable?    Yes  No

3.  How could the instrument be improved?

    _____

    _____

    _____

    _____

    _____

4.  Is your instrument unique or did you take the idea from a traditional instrument?

_____

**Fact file**

*Some Aboriginal Australian didgeridoos have been passed down from generation to generation as a symbol of peace and harmony in the group.*

The Amazon rainforest

## Objectives

- *Reads information and answers questions about the Amazon rainforest.*
- *Predicts difficulties confronting travellers in the Amazon and creates cartoons to illustrate possible scenarios.*

## Worksheet information

- Pupils will need to have some understanding of transpiration; that is, the process by which plants take carbon dioxide in through their foliage and release oxygen.
- The importance of this process as a counter to global warming may also need some explanation.
- The three countries of Guyana, Suriname and French Guyana are referred to as the Guyanas.
- Quiz questions relating to this section may be found on page xiv.

## Answers

### page 40

1. (a) Atlantic
   (b) Amazonia
   (c) It is about the size of Australia
   (d) 17 000–36 000 mm
   (e) the Peruvian Andes
2. (a) Teacher check. Possible answers may include: Because the rainforest 'breathes' in carbon dioxide and 'breathes' out oxygen. The Amazon rainforest produces 20% of the Earth's oxygen.
   (b) It changes carbon dioxide into oxygen.
   (c) There will be less oxygen in the Earth's atmosphere.
3. Brazil, Colombia, Peru, Bolivia, Venezuela, Ecuador and the Guyanas
4. Teacher check. Answers should include hot, wet, humid.

### page 41

1. (a) and (b) Teacher check

## Cross-curricular activities

- Pupils design clothes suitable for wearing in the Amazon rainforest.
- Pupils write newspaper reports about the Amazon River.
- Compare and contrast the climate where you live with that of the Amazon rainforest.

## Curriculum links

Page xix lists the main literacy and geography curriculum objectives covered by these activities. The final activity in this unit will help to teach the following curriculum objectives:

| England | English | KS 2 | • Use a range of writing forms. |
|---|---|---|---|
| Northern Ireland | Language and literacy | KS 2 | • Use a variety of writing forms. |
| Republic of Ireland | English | 5th/6th Class | • Write in a wide variety of genres. |
| Scotland | English | Level C | • Write in non-narrative forms in the context of other curricular areas. |
| Wales | English | KS 2 | • Write in a range of forms, in response to a wide range of stimuli. |

The Amazon rainforest in the northern central part of South America is found in the countries of Brazil, Colombia, Peru, Bolivia, Venezuela, Ecuador and the Guyanas. It covers an area about the size of Australia and represents one-third of the world's tropical rainforests. It is one of the world's greatest natural resources, producing about 20% of the Earth's oxygen by recycling carbon dioxide through its foliage. It has been described as the 'lungs of our planet'. This explains why the conservation of this area is a major world issue.

Known in Brazil, where it covers about half of the country, as **Amazonia**, the rainforest gets its name from the second longest river in the world; the mighty Amazon River. The Amazon is responsible for one-fifth of the fresh water entering the world's oceans and affects the salinity of the ocean for a distance of 160 kilometres. Beginning in the snow-capped Peruvian Andes and flowing 6 600 kilometres to the Atlantic Ocean at Belem in Brazil, the Amazon is the life force of the rainforest. The river is so deep that ocean liners can travel 3 700 kilometres inland. Whenever rain falls in the river basin, it drains through the rainforest into more than 1 000 tributaries to the Amazon River which is 8 to 56 kilometres wide, swelling at times to 320 to 480 kilometres at its mouth.

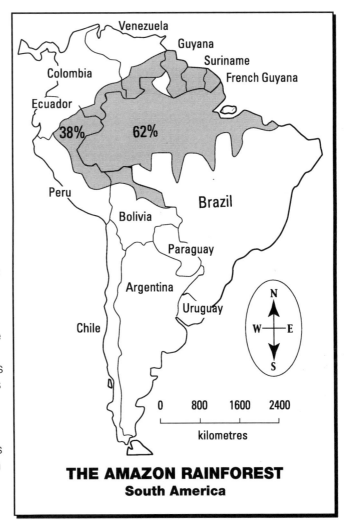

**THE AMAZON RAINFOREST**
**South America**

The tropical rainforest is warm and humid with an average temperature of 26 °C. It rains on about 200 days, resulting in a rainfall of 17 000 to 36 000 mm each year. When the snow on the mountains melts, it can cause the water in the river to rise 9 to 14 metres, covering tens of millions of hectares of rainforest with flood water. Some areas are underwater for nearly 10 months of the year.

In the past the ecosystem of the Amazon rainforest was protected by its isolation and because access was generally limited to navigable rivers. New roads, projects to settle millions of people in the region and the development of the cattle industry in the 1960s and 1970s threaten the biodiversity of this region.

Use the text on page 39 to answer the questions.

1. (a) Which ocean does the Amazon River flow into?

   

   (b) What do Brazilians call the Amazon rainforest?

   

   (c) How big is the Amazon rainforest?

   

   (d) What is the average annual rainfall in the Amazon rainforest?

   

   (e) Where does the Amazon River start?

   

2. (a) Explain why the Amazon rainforest is called the 'lungs of our planet'?

   _____

   _____

   _____

   (b) How does the rainforest recycle carbon dioxide?

   _____

   _____

   _____

   (c) What will happen if the rainforest is cleared?

   _____

   _____

   _____

3. Name the countries that contain part of the Amazon rainforest.

   

4. Write a description of the climate of the Amazon rainforest.

   

**Fact file**

*Half the rainfall in Amazonia returns to the atmosphere through the process of transpiration.*

1. Imagine that you are planning a trip through the Amazon.

   (a) List some of the problems that you would probably have to deal with.

   _____

   _____

   _____

   (b) Chose three problems and decide what you would do about each of them. Briefly state each problem and your solution to it, then illustrate it as a cartoon, using characters with speech balloons.

| *Problem* | |
|---|---|
| *Solution* | |
| *Problem* | |
| *Solution* | |
| *Problem* | |
| *Solution* | |

**Fact file**

*Only Egypt's Nile River is longer than the Amazon.*

## Objectives

- *Reads information and answers questions about the plants and animals of the Amazon rainforest.*
- *Researches to write a report on an Amazon animal.*

## Worksheet information

- Pupils would benefit from opportunities to discuss some of the economic factors affecting the destruction of the rainforests and the question of short-term as opposed to long-term goals. That is, the inhabitants need an income but if the trees are cut down and the timber sold, their finite resources will disappear. There is a similar problem with the cattle and agricultural industries.
- The potential value of the plants is enormous as is the tourist industry.
- Quiz questions relating to this section may be found on page xv.

## Answers

### page 44

1. (c), (d)

Answers may include:

2. (a) Excessive rainfall has washed away the minerals from the soil and it is only the continued decomposition of plants and animals on the forest floor that keeps the topsoil fertile. Once the land is cleared, this no longer occurs.

   (b) The soil is unsuitable for agriculture so they have to keep moving to newly-cleared land because their crops fail and they don't make any money.

3. (a) The canopy is so thick.

   (b) Orchids need sunlight to grow and there is very little on the forest floor, so they grow on the canopy.

   (c) Many of the plants have not yet been documented and they may have many uses, including the treatment of specific illnesses. If the rainforest is destroyed, they will be lost forever.

4. Teacher check

### page 45

Teacher check

## Cross-curricular activities

- Debate: 'Nothing can save the Amazon rainforest'.
- Create a class mural of the plants and animals of the Amazon rainforest.
- Discuss the roles of different scientists in the rainforest; for example, botanists, zoologists, anthropologists, palaeontologists, meteorologists, entymologists and pharmacologists.

## Curriculum links

Page xix lists the main literacy and geography curriculum objectives covered by these activities. The final activity in this unit will help to teach the following curriculum objectives:

| England | English | KS 2 | • Read non-fiction texts and use a range of writing forms, including reports. |
| Northern Ireland | Language and literacy | KS 2 | • Engage in a wide variety of reading activities and use a variety of writing forms, including reports. |
| Republic of Ireland | English | 5th/6th Class | • Explore non-fiction texts for various purposes and write in a wide variety of genres, including reports. |
| Scotland | English | Level C | • Read for information and write reports based on reading. |
| Wales | English | KS 2 | • Read and use a wide range of sources of information and write in a range of forms, including reports. |

The Amazon rainforest, a very special place, is home to the Earth's greatest number of different species of animals and plants. Although covering only 2% of the Earth, it has 30 million species of plants, animals and insects.

Excessive rainfall has washed away the minerals in the soil, making it acidic and infertile. Despite this, there have been 75 000 types of trees and 150 000 species of plants recorded in one square kilometre.

Only the top five centimetres of the soil is rich in nutrients from the rapid, ongoing decomposition of plants and animals on the forest floor. It is unsuitable for sustained agriculture and farmers constantly need to move on and clear more new land. This efficient ecosystem can be dramatically affected by the destruction of just one of its parts. The famous botanist, Charles Darwin (1809–1882), was fascinated by this area and aware of its importance. He wrote,

> 'The Amazon basin is a living thing. It lives in balance — consuming what it produces. If the balance is lost, it may die'.

Today, the land is being cleared for logging, mining, cattle ranches and agriculture and about 20% of the Amazon rainforest has been destroyed. This is of particular concern because many of the plants from this region have been found to be useful in the treatment of diseases and others have been destroyed before they could be tested. The main layer of the forest is the canopy, which is very dense, filtering out 80% of the sunlight. This is where many flowers and fruits grow.

The Amazon rainforest is home to 2.5 million insect species (including 6 000 butterflies), 2 000 mammals, fish (more than in the entire Atlantic Ocean) and birds (representing one-fifth of all the birds found on our planet).

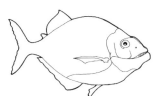

**Red-belly Piranha**

Piranhas are flesh-eating fish, native to the Amazon Basin. Their prey includes fish, insects, birds, lizards, rodents and dead flesh (carrion).

The danger of piranhas has been exaggerated, although people who have put their hands into an aquarium full of piranhas have been bitten. Perhaps the fish were underfed!

Piranhas range in colour from yellow, grey, blue, partly red to almost black and are from 15—60 cm long. They have a large lower jaw with lots of very sharp teeth. When one is broken off, a new one grows!

Predators include water snakes, turtles, otters, birds, other piranhas and people, because piranhas apparently taste so good!

Thousands of species of orchid grow in the Amazon rainforest.

They are considered by many to symbolise the beauty of the rainforest. However, they are not easy to see because they grow in the upper canopy and some of them bloom only rarely.

Orchids are surprisingly tough plants and are able to survive the intense heat of the upper canopy and even drying out.

Use the text on page 43 to answer the questions.

1. Tick the correct answers.

   ☐ (a) Rainforest land is great for farming.

   ☐ (b) More than half the Amazon rainforest has been cleared.

   ☐ (c) There are 30 million species of plants, animals and insects in the Amazon.

   ☐ (d) Flowers grow in the rainforest canopy.

2. (a) Why is the soil of the Amazon rainforest infertile?

   (b) How does this affect farming?

3. (a) Explain why very little sunlight reaches the rainforest floor.

   _____

   _____

   (b) Why do you think orchids grow in the canopy and not on the forest floor?

   _____

   _____

   _____

   (c) Why it is important to preserve the plants of the rainforest?

   _____

   _____

   _____

4. Write four interesting facts about piranhas.

   _____

   _____

   _____

   _____

> **Fact file**
>
> *100 hectares of Amazon rainforest can contain up to 1500 different plant species, as many as in the whole of the UK.*

*There are so many different fascinating animals in Amazonia that choosing one to research is challenging. The following shortlist may make this task easier.*

- Amazon River Turtle  • Wooly Monkey  • Tarantula  • Toucan  • Caiman
- Spider Monkey  • Leaf Cutter Ant  • Scarlet Macaw  • Harpy Eagle

My name is _____  Date _____

I chose to research _____

because _____

_____

_____

_____

### Anatomy

*Size:*

*Colour:*

*Features:*

### Habitat:

### Diet:

### Predators:

**Fact file**

*One in five of all the birds on Earth live in Amazonia.*

## Objectives

- *Reads information and answers questions about the exploration of the Amazon.*
- *Researches to write a diary and dramatises selected events.*

## Worksheet information

- Pupils will benefit from background information about Darwin and his theory of natural selection. Darwin spent five years sailing the world on the *Beagle*. He studied and collected thousands of animals and plants, including 13 species of finches he found on the Galapagos Islands, off the west coast of South America. He realised that the key to why they differed from the one species on the mainland was the environment. The birds had adapted to the unique environment of each island, by changing in ways that allowed them to get sufficient food to stay alive long enough to reproduce. This meant that the traits that enabled their survival were passed on to succeeding generations. These traits became more common and the population evolved. Darwin confirmed his theory by further research, some in the Amazon rainforest.
- Quiz questions relating to this section may be found on page xv.

## Answers

### page 48

1. (a)  false  (b) true  (c) false  (d) true  (e) true
2. (a)  Teacher check
   (b)  his theory of evolution based on natural selection
3. (a)  • The tribal women he saw fighting reminded Orellana of the Amazon warriors in mythology.
       • Some believe it came from the word 'amassona' meaning 'boat destroyer'.
   (b)  Teacher check

### page 49

1. Teacher check
2. Teacher check

## Cross-curricular activities

- Research the contribution Charles Darwin made to scientific knowledge.
- Produce a map showing the Galapagos Islands off the west coast of South America.
- Design a postage stamp featuring one of the early European explorers to the Amazon rainforest. Include visual information about his discoveries.

## Curriculum links

Page xix lists the main literacy and geography curriculum objectives covered by these activities. The final activity in this unit will help to teach the following curriculum objectives:

| England | English | KS 2 | • Use a range of writing forms. |
| Northern Ireland | Language and literacy | KS 2 | • Use a variety of writing forms, including diaries. |
| Republic of Ireland | English | 5th/6th Class | • Write in a wide variety of genres, including diaries. |
| Scotland | English | Level C | • Develop imaginative writing. |
| Wales | English | KS 2 | • Write in a range of forms, including diaries. |

The Amazon River, which provides access to the rainforest, wasn't discovered by Europeans until January 1500.

A Spanish navigator named Vicente Yanez Pinzon, who had sailed with Christopher Columbus on his famous, first journey of discovery to America, noticed that there was fresh water in the ocean 80 kilometres out to sea. He wanted to find its source, so he sailed towards the coast and explored the mouth of the river. He cut some of the beautiful, tall timber and returned home to Spain, but his country was not interested in making any territorial claim at that time.

In April of the same year, Pedro Alvares Cabral, a Portuguese sailor, officially claimed the land for Portugal. The following year, Portugal sent out an Italian sailor, Vespucci, who named the country 'Terra de Vera Cruz' (land of the true cross), but after he returned to Portugal with a cargo of red Brazilwood (braza = glowing coal), they started to call the country 'Brazil'.

Francisco de Orellana, a Spaniard who had joined a party of explorers searching for the legendary treasures of the golden city of El Dorado, led a group down the river looking for food in 1541 and continued on to explore the land because they couldn't get back upstream. He was responsible for naming the river. Most believe that he chose the name 'Amazon' because in one of the battles he fought against the Tapuyas tribe who lived there, he noticed that many of the fighters were women. This reminded him of the Greek myth about a race of warrior women called 'Amazons'. Some other people believe that the name came from the word, 'amassona', meaning 'boat destroyer'.

The first scientific data about the river, the plants and the people was recorded in 1759 by Charles de La Condamine, who accurately mapped the river and also discovered the milky sap from the trees that was later used to make rubber.

Scientists from all over the world became very interested in Amazonia after Alexander von Humboldt conducted the first tests on an electric eel in 1800. He had discovered the strange creatures by stepping on one.

Charles Darwin was so excited about all that he saw in the Amazon rainforest that in 1832 he wrote:

> *Wonder, astonishment and sublime devotion, fill and elevate the mind.*

He and an English scientist, Alfred Wallace, both developed theories of evolution through natural selection based, in part, on thousands of new species they discovered in the Amazon rainforest. They both presented papers about their startling new theories in London in 1858.

Use the text on page 47 to answer the questions.

1. True or false?

   (a) Christopher Columbus discovered the Amazon River.

   True ◯ False ◯

   (b) Pinzon took some Amazon rainforest timber back to Spain.

   True ◯ False ◯

   (c) Orellana named the Amazon River 'Terra de Vera Cruz'.

   True ◯ False ◯

   (d) Condamine discovered the sap later used in making rubber.

   True ◯ False ◯

   (e) Charles Darwin discovered many new species in the Amazon rainforest.

   True ◯ False ◯

2. (a) Why was Charles Darwin so impressed with the Amazon rainforest?

   _____

   _____

   _____

   _____

   _____

   (b) What resulted from his research there?

   _____

   _____

   _____

   _____

   _____

3. (a) What are two theories about how the Amazon got its name?

   (b) Which one do you think is true? Explain.

   _____

   _____

   _____

   **Fact file**

   *There were an estimated 10 million Indians living in the Amazon rainforest five centuries ago. There are less than 200 000 today.*

1. Read the paragraph about Orellana on page on 47 again and research further information about his exploration and naming of the Amazon. Use this information and your imagination to write a diary covering two days of his journey. You may choose to tell about his encounter with the warrior women, discuss his thoughts about the tropical weather or describe any difficulties or successes you think he may have experienced. Add illustrations to your diary if you think they are appropriate.

Date _____

Date _____

2. Choose one day from your diary to dramatise with a small group. As you are the author, you may like to be the director and have others play the characters.

**Fact file**

*American president, Theodore Roosevelt, accompanied by his son Kermit, led an expedition to the Amazon in 1913–1914. Roosevelt contracted malaria and he and all of his team were lucky to survive the journey.*

## Objectives

• *Reads information and answers questions about the Daintree rainforest.*
• *Completes an Internet challenge to determine the flora being described.*

## Worksheet information

• Queensland boasts two World Heritage sights that actually meet. The Wet Tropics meets the Great Barrier Reef in a spectacular fashion along the coastline as the forest meets the sea.

For the activity on page 53, Daintree flora Internet challenge, the pupils will need access to the Internet. Pupils may find more success with this activity by working in small groups. Two helpful websites include:

<www.rainforest-australia.com> and <www.daintreerainforest.com>

• Quiz questions relating to this section may be found on page xvi.

## Answers

**page 52**

1.  (a) false        (b) true
    (c) true         (d) true
    (e) false (1930s)  (f) false

2.  (a) Scientists can support the theory of Gondwanaland because they have found many plant fossils of the same species and chronology in Africa, South America, Antarctica, Australia and India.

    (b) Teacher check — Possible answers may include – The shapes of the continents appear to be part of a jigsaw puzzle that would roughly fit back together; e.g. north-west coast of Africa and east coast of North America; south part of Africa and east coast of South America.

3.  • May contain plants with anti-cancer properties.
    • 13 species of birds found nowhere else in the world.
    • More primitive plant groups than any other rainforest in the world.

• Flowering plants that existed during the dinosaur period.
• 135 million years old.
• Records of eight major stages of plant evolution.

4.  Possible answers:
    **Queensland government**
    – economic gain
    – jobs (less unemployment)
    **Federal government**
    – conserve environment
    – tourism for country and state

**page 53**

1.  Strangler fig          2.  Idiot fruit
3.  Blue Quandong       4.  Wait-a-while vine
5.  Stinging tree          6.  Burrawong palm
7.  Red flowering mistletoe

## Cross-curricular activities

• Pupils find images of one or more of the flora described on page 53 on the Internet or from the library. Pupils use sharp lead pencils to sketch the plants on art paper, then label the sketches and mount them onto coloured card.

• Pupils write a narrative piece imagining that they are one of the explorers who first ventured into the Daintree forest in 1897. The piece must include descriptions of the dense, impenetrable forest and include their motive for being there.

• In the 1930s, pioneering families began to settle on the land, non-native fruit was grown and the timber industry was soaring. In groups, pupils consider how these activities would have affected the ecosystem of the rainforest. On large sheets of paper, pupils write the headings; plants, birds, insects and mammals, and write suggestions on how each would have been affected by the changes that occurred in the thirties.

**Challenge:** In small groups, pupils research the topic of 'evolution' and present a brief report to the class explaining the main ideas.

## Curriculum links

Page xix lists the main literacy and geography curriculum objectives covered by these activities. The final activity in this unit will help to teach the following curriculum objectives:

| England | English | KS 2 | • Use ICT-based reference materials. |
|---|---|---|---|
| Northern Ireland | Language and literacy | KS 2 | • Read electronic texts on the Internet. |
| Republic of Ireland | English | 5th/6th Class | • Find information through the use of IT. |
| Scotland | English | Level C | • Read for specific information. |
| | ICT | Level D | • Use a search engine. |
| Wales | English | KS 2 | • Use ICT-based reference materials. |

### The Daintree – Profile

- *Found north of Cairns in Tropical Far North Queensland, Australia*
- *Covers 12 000 square kilometres*
- *World Heritage listed in 1988*
- *Over 135 million years old*
- *430 species of birds (13 found nowhere else in the world)*
- *Average rainfall of 2013 mm a year—torrential downpours occur regularly.*
- *Average temperature 28 °C—mild due to protective canopy layer of tall trees.*
- *It is believed that there are plants in the Daintree that have anti-cancer properties.*

The Daintree contains many rare species of plants and animals. Many of the species originated when Australia was still part of Gondwanaland.

Gondwana was a huge landmass that began separating into the separate continents about 120 million years ago.

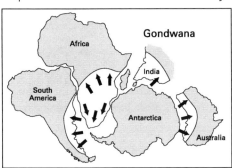

About 40 to 50 million years ago, Australia settled into its final form and position. Scientists can support this theory because they have found many plant fossils of the same species and same chronology (time) in Africa, South America, Antarctica, Australia and India.

Biologists consider the Daintree rainforest to be a living museum, containing more primitive plant groups than any other rainforest in the world. Botanists have found flowering plants which are thought to be 100 million years old and existed around the time of the dinosaurs. Because Australia was reasonably stable during the evolution of flowering plants, these forests existed undisturbed for millions of years.

It is believed that the Daintree holds an almost complete record of the eight major stages of plant evolution—the only place on Earth where this is found.

### Daintree time line
#### since European arrival

**1770**
First European record of area by Sir Joseph Banks.

**Early 1800s**
Explorers search forest for areas to settle in and for gold but find it too difficult to penetrate.

**1897**
Areas of the Daintree advertised as freehold land to attract settlers.

**1930s**
Pioneering families begin to settle on land. Bananas, watermelons and pineapples grown. The timber industry in area begins and causes economic boom!

**1980s**
Conflict between the timber industry and conservationists begins.

**1987**
Australian federal government nominates area to be World Heritage area. Queensland state government fights backs and takes federal government to the High Court.

**1988**
The Wet Tropics is given a World heritage listing. The Daintree is safe!

Use the text on page 51 to answer the questions.

1. Tick 'true' or 'false'.

   (a) The Daintree rainforest is found south of Cairns.
   - True
   - False

   (b) The canopy from the tall trees keeps the temperature mild.
   - True
   - False

   (c) Some flowering plants from the Daintree existed in the time of dinosaurs.
   - True
   - False

   (d) Early explorers hoped to find gold in the forest.
   - True
   - False

   (e) The economic boom of the timber trade occurred in 1897.
   - True
   - False

   (f) The Australian federal government wanted the forest used for timber.
   - True
   - False

2. (a) What evidence supports the theory that the continents were once a part of a large landmass known as Gondwana?

   _____

   _____

   _____

   _____

   (b) Look at the diagram of Gondwana. Can you see any other evidence that may support the theory?

   _____

   _____

   _____

   _____

3. List three reasons why the Daintree rainforest is unique and important.

   _____

   _____

   _____

4. The Queensland state government took the Australian federal government to the High Court to try to prevent the Daintree rainforest from being on the protected World Heritage list.

   List reasons why you think each government had different ideas about the Daintree forest.

| Queensland state government | Australian federal government |
|---|---|
|  |  |

---

**Fact file**

*Found in the Daintree, the Stinging tree has glass-like hairs that embed into your skin. The effects are extremely painful and can last for months. There is no known antidote.*

## Daintree flora Internet challenge!

1. Read each description below of the flora found in the Daintree rainforest. Use search engines on the Internet (such as Google™) to discover which type of vegetation is being described.

---

**1. What am I?**

- I am a type of fig.
- I am believed to be 500 to 600 years old.
- My seed germinates high in a tree.
- I drop long cable-like roots that twist around my host tree, eventually killing it.
- My name sounds murderous!

*I am the* _____.

---

**2. What am I?**

- I am a fruit.
- I was discovered in 1970 when cattle began dying after eating me.
- My large seeds produce poisons.
- My name suggests that I am a fool.

*I am the* _____.

---

**3. What am I?**

- I am a giant tree of the rainforest.
- I bear a colourful fruit about 3 cm in diameter.
- I shield the plants below me from the sun.
- I drop red leaves.
- My name includes a colour.

*I am the* _____.

---

**4. What am I?**

- I hang from the tallest tree to the forest floor.
- I have small spikes that will tear your clothes and rip into your skin.
- My other name is the 'Lawyer vine'.
- Bushwalkers must be very 'patient' near me.

*I am the* _____.

---

**5. What am I?**

- I am a tree.
- I stand between one and five metres high.
- My heart-shaped leaves are covered in thick prickly hairs.
- The tips of my prickles can break off into your skin and release a painful poison.

*I am the* _____.

---

**6. What am I?**

- I am a palm.
- I produce highly toxic seeds.
- I am a member if the cycad family.
- I am found on the rainforest floor.
- I have large cones that look like green pineapples.

*I am the* _____.

---

**7. What am I?**

- I begin as a seed in the canopy of the forest.
- I take water and nutrients from my host tree.
- I have spectacular red flowers.
- There is a bird named after me.
- My name may remind you of Christmas.

*I am the* _____.

---

2. Other interesting facts I have learned about flora of the Daintree include:

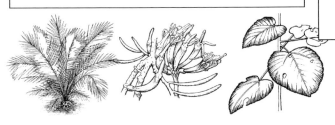

**Fact file**

*75% of Australia's tropical rainforests have been cleared since the 1700s.*

## The Daintree rainforest — Fauna of the Daintree

### Objectives

- *Reads information and answers questions about the fauna of the Daintree rainforest.*
- *Designs a greeting card that represents the rainforest and its fauna.*

### Worksheet information

- The southern boundary of the Daintree is the Daintree River. The eastern boundary is the Great Barrier Reef. The northern boundary of the Daintree is the Bloomfield River. The Daintree contains significant features which are rare in other parts of the world. Some of these include:

    • swamps    • sclerophyll forests    • woodlands    • mangroves

    Many different types of species live in a rainforest area such as the Daintree.

    To introduce fauna of the Daintree rainforest, discuss the importance of the cassowary (see information on page 15). This is explained clearly and humorously in the poem *Hasslebarry and the cassowary* by Laurence Horner, found on the website <www.dctta.asn.au/cassowarypoem.htm>.

    Discuss the importance of the cassowary's function of collecting and dropping seeds on to the rainforest floor.

- Quiz questions relating to this section may be found on page xvi.

### Answers

***page 56***

1. (a) witchetty grub (b) bandicoot (c) rufous owl (d) spotted cuscus (e) giant tree frog (f) cassowary

2,

| rufous owl | sugar gliders, cockatoos, beetles, flying foxes, kookaburras |
|---|---|
| cassowary | large fruit |
| bandicoot | insects, spiders, worms |
| sugar glider | sweet nectar, honey, insects |
| giant tree frog | insects |
| spotted cuscus | vegetation, insects, nectar |

3. • Preys on large birds such as kookaburras and cockatoos, and sugar gliders and flying foxes
   • Protects its nest aggressively
   • Invades nests of other birds and eats their young.

4. Eats over 100 species of large fruit and disperses the seeds throughout the forest. New fruit trees and plants will grow from these seeds.

5. (a) bandicoot, spotted cuscus, sugar glider
   (b) Teacher check

6. Teacher check

***page 57***

Teacher check

### Cross-curricular activities

- Pupils use the website <www.rainforestrescue.org.au> to find out more about the 'Buy back' system. In groups, pupils debate: Should the people who privately own part of the Daintree rainforest be forced to sell it back to the government?

- Choose three of the animals from page 55 and look on the Internet to find where else these animals can be found in the world. On a world map, record this information using colour-coded keys to distinguish between the animals.

- Write definitions for the words 'extinct', 'endangered' and 'threatened'. The cassowary is on the endangered species list. Find five other rainforest animals that are classified as endangered or threatened.

### Curriculum links

Page xix lists the main literacy and geography curriculum objectives covered by these activities. The final activity in this unit will help to teach the following curriculum objectives:

| England | Art and design | KS 2 | • Use a variety of methods to design and make images. |
|---|---|---|---|
| Northern Ireland | Art | KS 2 | • Use a range of materials to realise their ideas and intentions. |
| Republic of Ireland | Visual arts | 5th/6th Class | • Make drawings based on themes and explore colour. |
| Scotland | Art and design | Level C | • Explore a range of drawing techniques using a variety of materials. |
| Wales | Art | KS 2 | • Plan and make images using various materials for a variety of purposes. |

The Daintree, with its woodlands, mangroves, rivers and a forest that meets the ocean, is the habitat for many amazing species of animals, including some considered to be rare. Here are just a few examples.

## Cassowary

Listed as an endangered species, the flightless cassowary stands approximately 1.75 metres high. It has a pale blue head, a black body and red wattles hanging from its neck. The cassowary plays an essential role in the rainforest. With its diet being mainly large fruit, it collects seeds from over 100 fruit plants when it eats and disperses them throughout the forest. Cassowarys have spikes on each foot up to 12 cm long that can become weapons if the bird becomes agitated. Never turn your back on a cassowary—face it and back away slowly!

Threats to the cassowary include dogs, motor vehicles and traps built for feral pigs.

## Spotted cuscus

With its unique 'two-thumbed' hands, the spotted cuscus (similar to a sloth) is able to cling upside down from the branches of trees.

Approximately 80 cm long, this shy creature is nocturnal and can be found sleeping in trees during the day. The cuscus has brown and black spots on its back and is covered in a tan-coloured fur. Its diet includes vegetation, insects and nectar.

## Rufous owl

A nocturnal creature, the rufous owl can weigh up to 1.3 kilograms. Although known as a shy bird, it often invades the nests of other birds and eats their young. Its prey includes blue-winged kookaburras, white cockatoos, flying foxes, sugar gliders and beetles. The owl will defend its own nest aggressively.

## Bandicoot

Only the length of your ruler (30 cm), these nocturnal grey-furred creatures hop around the forest like a kangaroo. Bandicoots are shy, hiding in hollow logs. With their long noses, bandicoots can sniff out food such as insects, spiders and worms from the forest floor.

## Sugar glider

These small grey creatures are about 20 cm in length and enjoy feeding on sweet nectar, honey and insects. A special membrane, resembling wing-like flaps, enables the possums to glide from tree to tree.

## Giant tree frog

With a mating call that resembles a dog's bark, this brilliant green frog is the largest variety of frog on earth. Living wherever water is near, this 14-centimetre frog enjoys eating insects.

## Beauty and the beast

The beautiful Ulysses butterfly is an iridescent, metallic blue butterfly.
The fat, white witchetty grub lives under bark and is eaten as 'bush tucker'.

Use the text on page 55 to answer the questions.

1. Match the description with the correct animal.

| | |
|---|---|
| (a) Described by some as 'bush tucker'. • | • bandicoot |
| (b) This shy creature likes to hide in hollow logs. • | • spotted cuscus |
| (c) Its diet includes young sugar gliders and cockatoos. • | • cassowary |
| (d) A nocturnal creature that is similar to a sloth. • | • giant tree frog |
| (e) Has a mating call that resembles a dog's bark. • | • witchetty grub |
| (f) Never turn your back on this 1.75-metre tall creature! • | • rufous owl |

2. Complete the table about the diet of the fauna of the Daintree.

| rufous owl | sugar gliders, cockatoos, beetles, flying foxes, kookaburras |
|---|---|
| cassowary | |
| bandicoot | |
| sugar glider | |
| giant tree frog | |
| spotted cuscus | |

3. List two behaviours of the rufous owl that show it is perhaps not as 'shy' as it looks.

   • _____

   _____

   • _____

   _____

4. Explain why the cassowary is essential to the Daintree rainforest's survival.

5. A marsupial is a mammal whose young wiggle across their mother's belly to search for milk and stay in a pouch-like fold of skin on their mother's stomach until they are fully developed.

   (a) Which three of the animals described on page 55 do you think are most likely marsupials?

   (b) Give reasons for your answers.

6. If you were offered a witchetty grub to taste, would you eat it?

   Absolutely! | No way!

   **Fact file**
   *Tropical rainforests covers about 6% of the Earth's surface and yet they contain over 50% of the Earth's species.*

*Some parts of the Daintree rainforest are privately owned by people who can use the land however they wish. Rainforest Rescue is an organisation that is promoting the 'Buy Back' of this land. The Australian government has been able to buy back some of the land which is now safe from housing and road developments, but more money is needed.*

1. Design a greeting card that could be sold by Rainforest Rescue to raise money to buy back the privately owned parts of the Daintree.

   Your card needs to be neat, colourful and eye-catching! It also must:

   - *contain art that represents the rainforest*
   - *include at least one animal found in the rainforest*
   - *state how money from the sale of the card will be used (generally this is found on the back cover)*

2. Choose one or more of the animals from the Daintree rainforest to include on your card. You may need to use the Internet or library to find pictures to help you.

| *estuarine crocodile* ☐ | *cassowary* ☐ | *golden orb spider* ☐ | *bandicoot* ☐ |
| *azure kingfisher* ☐ | *musty rat-kangaroo* ☐ | *Ulysses butterfly* ☐ | *goanna* ☐ |
| *spotted cuscus* ☐ | *giant tree frog* ☐ | *sugar glider* ☐ | *rufous owl* ☐ |

**Front cover design (ideas and sketches)**    **Inside text and/or art**

**Back cover text**

3. Now use your draft ideas and create your greeting card on a separate sheet of card. If available, word process the text and glue it onto your card.

**Fact file**

*A landowner of a section of the Daintree cleared a plot of land and, without realising, made a tree from the red cedar family extinct.*

## Objectives

- *Reads information and answers questions about the destruction of the rainforest.*
- *Completes a crossword about the destruction of the rainforest using words taken from a text.*

## Worksheet information

- As pupils research information about the destruction of the rainforest, they will encounter many websites devoted to saving the rainforests at any cost. Pupils will need to try to be objective when obtaining information before forming their own opinions.
- Quiz questions relating to this section may be found on page xvii.

## Answers

### page 60

1. (a) having no equal; standing alone in comparison with others

   (b) the act of creating more urban areas such as cities or towns

   (c) farming in which the produce is consumed by the farmer's family, leaving little or no surplus for marketing

   (d) likely to be sold in great numbers

   (e) a common mineral, tin oxide ($S_nO_2$), the principal ore of tin

   (f) to strip the land of forests or trees

   (g) native; originating in and characterising a particular region or country

2. overpopulation, subsistence farming, increased need for commercial products, commercial logging, cattle grazing

3-4. Teacher check

### page 61

**Across**
3. rainforests 4. population 5. subsistence 6. fuel
7. agriculture 10. urbanisation 11. logging 13. roads
14. medicines

**Down**
1. deforestation 2. destruction 8. hardwood 9. timber
10. unique 12. commercial

## Cross-curricular activities

- Pupils write narratives from the viewpoint of trees which are being cut down or indigenous people who are losing their traditional lands.
- Pupils use percussion instruments to compile pieces of music which tell the story of the loss of plants and animals as rainforest areas are cut down. Pupils use body movement to accompany the music.
- Pupils compile a list of factual information from reliable sources about the destruction of the rainforest.

## Curriculum links

Page xix lists the main literacy and geography curriculum objectives covered by these activities. The final activity in this unit will help to teach the following curriculum objectives:

| England | Geography | KS 2 | • Use appropriate geographical vocabulary. |
|---|---|---|---|
| Northern Ireland | Geography | KS 2 | • Use precise subject specific vocabulary. |
| Republic of Ireland | English | 5th/6th Class | • Experience a growing elaboration and sophistication in the use of vocabulary. |
| Scotland | Society | Level E | • Use appropriate specialist vocabulary. |
| Wales | Geography | KS 2 | • Use and extend their geographical vocabulary. |

Rainforests are extremely complex, unique environments supporting a treasure trove of plants and animals. Unfortunately, the gradual clearing of the land of forests or trees (deforestation), for a variety of reasons, has seen the destruction of vast areas of rainforest around the world.

Since 1980, the population of the world has increased by 30%, and will continue to grow. With this increase in population has come an increase in the number of forest products needed, forcing more areas of rainforest to be cut down.

As a direct result of urbanisaton, areas which were previously uninhabited, such as rainforest areas, are now being used to support many small subsistence farmers. As rainforest soils are poor, farmers cannot reuse the same land each year. Instead, they are forced to clear new areas of the forest each year.

Tropical rainforests supply a great variety of commercial and non-commercial products, including timber, wood for fuel, fruits, vegetables, nuts and spices, medicines, ingredients to make chewing gum, rubber, chocolate, sugar, rope and basket-making materials. Chemicals from leaves, flowers and seeds of rainforest plants are used to make perfumes, cosmetics, soaps, shampoos, disinfectants, detergents and polishes. Other products such as iron, manganese, cassiterite, bauxite, gold, copper and nickel are also taken from rainforest areas.

Commercial logging is the largest cause of rainforest destruction. Teak, mahogany, rosewood and other hardwood timbers for furniture and building materials are in great demand. Most rainforests are cleared by chainsaws, bulldozers and fires to obtain the valuable timbers, which are used all over the world. Other wood products including charcoal and wood for fuel are also obtained. The need to construct dams and roads for transporting timber is also a contributing factor to rainforest destruction.

As human expansion continues, large areas are constantly cleared to provide grazing land for cattle for beef export markets such as hamburger chains. Large-scale agriculture projects such as banana and coffee plantations add to the deforestation problem.

Other factors contributing to the destruction include natural disasters, war and poverty.

*The destruction of tropical rainforest areas has many effects:*

- *loss of unique plant and animal species,*
- *climate and weather changes locally and worldwide,*
- *loss of indigenous people and their unique cultures,*
- *soil erosion,*
- *air and water pollution.*

Some experts believe that if deforestation continues at the current rate, within the next 100 years there will no longer be any rainforests.

The destruction of
the rainforest | **The destruction of the
rainforest – 2**

Use the text on page 59 to answer the questions.

1.  Use your dictionary to write the meaning of the following words:

    (a) unique: _____

    (b) urbanisation: _____

    (c) subsistence farming: _____

    _____

    (d) commercial: _____

    (e) cassiterite: _____

    (f) deforestation: _____

    (g) indigenous: _____

2.  List five reasons for the destruction of the rainforest.

    •  _____

    •  _____

    •  _____

    •  _____

    •  _____

3.  Write sentences to explain how the factors listed below may have contributed to the destruction of the rainforest:

    | *natural disasters* |
    | --- |
    |  |

    | *war* |
    | --- |
    |  |

    | *poverty* |
    | --- |
    |  |

4.  In small groups, discuss the possible effects of the total destruction of the rainforests.

    ┌─ **Fact file** ─┐

    *One hectare (2.4 acres) of rainforest is destroyed every second — that's the equivalent of more than two football pitches!*

*Complete the crossword using information from page 59*

**Down**

1. The act of stripping land of forests or trees.

2. Demolition or annihilation.

8. A particular type of timber specifically used for building.

9. Wood of growing trees for use in building.

10. Unequalled, rare.

12. Likely to be sold in great numbers.

**Across**

3. Dense forests found in tropical and temperate areas with high humidity and rainfall most of the year.

4. The total number of people living in a city, town, country or area.

5. This type of farming feeds the farmer and his family with little left over for selling.

6. Material used to maintain a fire.

7. The cultivation of the land to raise crops or livestock.

10. Creating more areas of cities or towns.

11. The process of cutting down trees to get logs for timber.

13. Building these for transport can cause extra damage to the rainforests.

14. Products to treat illness, often created from ingredients taken from plants.

**Fact file**

*Seventy-five per cent of Australia's rainforest has been cleared since the late 1700s.*

## Objectives

- *Reads information and answers questions about preserving the rainforest.*
- *Reads and completes information about 'healing' plants.*

## Worksheet information

- The intention of this section is to help pupils to gain some understanding of the importance of the rainforest to the rest of the world and to present a few ideas for preserving the rainforest. The solution—if there is one—may be a combination of suggestions.
- The Amazon rainforest has been called 'The lungs of our planet' because it produces more than 20% of the world's oxygen.
- Most of our current plant-derived drugs were discovered by studying the traditional use of plants by indigenous people. Scientists have often worked with rainforest tribal shamans (medicine men) and herbal healers to learn their knowledge.
- Indigenous people have, for centuries, lived in the rainforest, gathering food, hunting, using plants for a variety of uses and carrying out sustainable agriculture without destroying the rainforest. It has been suggested that to employ some of their ancient methods of sustainable agriculture would ensure some degree of preservation.
- Some experts have suggested that creating a large enough market for medicinal plants, fruits, nuts, oil and other sustainable resources may make rainforest areas more valuable alive than cut and burnt.
- Quiz questions relating to this section may be found on page xvii.

## Answers

### page 64

1. (a) ... plant and animal life.
   (b) ... drug-yielding plants.
   (c) ... there will not be sufficient oxygen to breathe.
   (d) ... evaporation; rain; floods; drought; erosion of the soil.
   (e) ... the protective layer of dead and decaying vegetation.
   (f) indigenous people.
2. Teacher check

### page 65

1. Teacher check
2. (a) rosemary (b) aloe vera (c) lavender
   (d) echinacea (e) ginger (f) garlic (g) aloe vera
   (h) lavender (i) rosemary (j) ginger
3. Teacher check

## Cross-curricular activities

- Groups of pupils are divided into teams to debate the topic 'The rainforest should be preserved' or 'The rainforest can be used as a source of consumer products without destroying it'.
- Pupils interview their parents, grandparents, great-grandparents or elderly neighbours to investigate natural remedies for ailments, cleaning products, insecticides, beauty or hygiene products.
- Pupils research, collect and collate a class resource of recipes for natural remedies, cleaning products, gardening products, insecticides, beauty or hygiene products.

## Curriculum links

Page xix lists the main literacy and geography curriculum objectives covered by these activities. The final activity in this unit will help to teach the following curriculum objectives:

| England | English | KS 2 | • Scan texts to find information and use ICT-based reference materials. |
|---|---|---|---|
| Northern Ireland | Language and literacy | KS 2 | • Use different reading skills, including scanning, and read electronic texts on the Internet. |
| Republic of Ireland | English | 5th/6th Class | • Develop study skills such as scanning and find information through the use of IT. |
| Scotland | English | Level C | • Develop ability to scan for specific information. |
| | ICT | Level D | • Use a search engine. |
| Wales | English | KS 2 | • Use scanning to locate information and use ICT-based reference materials. |

### Why try to preserve the rainforest?

The rainforest is the world's richest source of plant and animal life. It is the most productive and complex ecosystem on Earth. It is home to 50 to 70% of all our life forms. Once the rainforest is eradicated, untold species of plants and animals will also be eradicated. Many even now are extinct or endangered. Animals such as the giant otter, jaguar and woolly spider monkey are becoming increasingly rare as a result of the destruction of the rainforest.

*Giant otter*

Tropical rainforests provide more drug-yielding plants for medicines than any other ecosystem; for example, the rosy periwinkle from Madagascar provides two agents for combating tumours. Other plants are used for drugs and medicines to combat illnesses such as leukaemia, strokes, seizures, depression, Alzheimer's disease, malaria and even the common headache! Many plants have not yet been investigated regarding their ability to provide life-saving drugs and medicines, and will never be, if they are destroyed.

Plants in the rainforest change carbon dioxide into clean air and absorb carbon dioxide which they store in their roots, leaves, stems and branches. This interdependence exists among all plants, animals and humans on earth. Increased amounts of carbon dioxide in the atmosphere contribute to the 'greenhouse effect' and cause global temperatures to rise. Destroying rainforest plants affects all life on earth!

Rainforests capture, store and recycle rain. Evaporation is the main method used to do this. This helps prevent floods, drought and erosion of the soil. Some experts also believe that the destruction of tropical rainforests around the Equator and in the northern temperate zones could decrease the amount of rainfall around the world, leading to climate change.

Soils in rainforests are protected by dead and decaying vegetation which contains essential minerals. Once deforestation occurs, this protective layer is swept away by rain or wind to leave 'human-made' deserts, unsuitable for agriculture and lacking the ability to sustain plant and animal life.

Indigenous rainforest people are losing their traditional way of life, including knowledge from shamans, as their traditional homes are destroyed and urban movement continues. Violent confrontations occur between traditional 'rubber tappers' and newly arrived ranchers. It is thought that there are over 1 000 or more indigenous groups around the world on the verge of extinction as a result of the destruction of the rainforest.

### How can we help to preserve the rainforest?

No single easy solution exists for this global problem. Thought must be given to long-term planning regarding better forest management, increasing the productivity of cleared rainforest lands, rehabilitating the habitat of endangered species or providing alternative habitat for them, expanding protected areas of rainforest, trying to find ways to use some existing forest in a more sustainable way and encouraging governments to enforce laws or make policies which protect rainforests.

# Preserving the rainforest - 2

Use the text on page 63 to answer the questions.

1. Complete these sentences.

(a) The rainforest is the world's richest source of _____

_____

(b) Tropical rainforests provide more ___,_____ for

medicines than any other ecosystem.

(c) Destroying rainforest plants affects other animals on Earth because

_____

(d) Rainforests recycle rainwater by _____, capture and store

_____ which helps to prevent _____, _____

and _____

(e) Deforestation of the rainforest allows wind and rain to sweep away

_____

(f) The traditional way of life of _____ is being

lost as the rainforest, their traditional home, is being destroyed.

2. Explain how these solutions may help to alleviate the problem of the destruction of the rainforest:

- better forest management:

_____

_____

_____

_____

- increasing productivity of cleared rainforest lands:

_____

_____

_____

_____

- rehabilitating the habitat of endangered species:

_____

_____

_____

_____

- finding ways to use some existing forest in a more sustainable way:

_____

_____

_____

_____

_____

**Fact file**

*For every tropical plant species that becomes extinct, 20 insect species may not survive.*

# Cures from nature
**Preserving the rainforest**

*As more rainforests are destroyed, so too are the ways of life of the indigenous people who inhabit them. These cultures are irreplaceable.*

*When a medicine man – shaman – dies without passing his arts on to the next generation, the tribe (and the world) loses thousands of years of knowledge about medicinal plants. It is said that 'each time a rainforest medicine man dies, it is as if a library has burned down'.*

1. Read the information about healing plants below.

- The **aloe vera** plant contains a gel useful for healing wounds. It is a mixture of an antibiotic, astringent and coagulating agents. It aids in the treatment of burns, insect stings and poison ivy.
- **Echinacea** is a preventive herb. It contains a natural antibiotic which means that it is an effective broad-based infection fighter.
- **Garlic** is a member of the onion family grown and used to prevent and treat colds and flu and to help superficial infections.
- **Ginger** is used by herbalists for many purposes. It is a good digestive aid and helps stomach cramps and nausea. It is often made into ale.
- **Lavender** is a bushy shrub bearing small lavender-purple flowers. It is used for its oil and believed to be a useful remedy for restlessness and insomnia.
- **Rosemary** is a scented shrub usually with narrow grey-green leaves. Dried rosemary leaves are distilled to make perfumes and medicines. It is commonly thought to improve mental fatigue and reduce forgetfulness.

2. Write the plant from the list which best suits the purpose below.

(a) forgetfulness

_____

(b) sunburn

_____

(c) insomnia

_____

(d) severely infected cut

_____

(e) stomach ache

_____

(f) cold

_____

(g) bee sting

_____

(h) perfumed soap

_____

(i) concentration

_____

(j) diarrhoea

_____

3. Use library or Internet resources to investigate the healing properties of these herbs: St John's wort, peppermint, fennel, dandelion, sage, parsley, nutmeg and cinnamon.

**Fact file**

*In 1990, the president of Brazil signed laws to allow more than 2 million hectares of rainforest to be managed by rubber tappers, nut gatherers and others whose livelihoods depended on traditional rainforest harvest.*

**Prim-Ed Publishing    www.prim-ed.com**

**RAINFORESTS**    **65**